Practical Transmitters for Novices

John Case, GW4HWR

Radio Society of Great Britain

Published by the Radio Society of Great Britain, Cranborne Road, Potters Bar, Herts EN6 3JE.

First published 1995

ISBN 1 872309 21 6

Cover design: Geoff Korten Design.
Watercolour-effect photo on front cover: Hilary Claytonsmith, G4JKS.
Illustrations: Derek Cole and Bob Ryan, Radio Society of Great Britain.
Production and typography: Ray Eckersley, Seven Stars Publishing.

Printed in Great Britain by Bell & Bain Ltd, Glasgow.

Contents

Preface

Originally it was intended that this book should contain a selection of 'easy-to-build' transmitters but, as work progressed, the need for some explanation of the function of the projects was recognised. Some theory was added to help with the understanding, and gradually the present form evolved. It is quite possible that some interested amateurs will find the book useful as a simple textbook of transmitter techniques, even if they do not intend (before reading!) to make up any of the projects. Others may wish to experiment with some of the simpler designs. I hope that everyone will find something of interest. Every effort has been made to present both the theory and practice in easily understood language.

Anyone intending to follow some or all of the projects would be advised to gather as many catalogues as possible, even though this may mean spending some of the precious funds! Some are free but others, like those from Cirkit and Maplin, are fairly expensive (both are obtainable from most branches of W H Smith), though they make very useful reference books. There is no need to buy new ones each year as most items used in basic construction remain unchanged over long periods and even the prices are remarkably stable.

Thanks are due to all those who have helped with this book. They include Mike Dixon, G3PFR, for supplying the material for Chapters 9 and 10 on microwave projects; Steve Price, G4BWE, for the use of the major part of his article (originally published in *Radio Communication* December 1991 and January 1992) describing the construction of an 80m transmitter; Terry Cross, GW4LFW, and Martin Williams for their help in producing some of the PCB foil patterns, transparencies and overlays; the members of the Training and Education Committee for input and encouragement; and my wife, Joan, BRS87511, for her tolerance of the masses of papers and my time crouched over a hot word processor.

John Case, GW4HWR

Chapter 1

Methods of construction

Various methods used by constructors are described in this chapter. Details of those methods not used for the projects are described in rather more detail while the remainder will be covered fully in the sections dealing with the projects.

Printed circuit board

This is the professional method of setting up an electronic circuit. The interconnections are in the form of a copper foil which has been etched to the exact pattern required by the circuit in hand. This has the great advantage of making it very easy to duplicate results, as the position of the wiring and components is controlled by the layout of the copper tracks and the holes for the components drilled in the board. The stability of this form of construction is in itself a disadvantage to the experimenter as it is difficult to make alterations to a circuit once the PCB has been etched and drilled. This is an ideal method of construction once the circuit has been confirmed but is often rejected by the home constructor because of the work involved in making the board for just one final circuit.

Veroboard™

This is a board about 1.5mm thick made from insulation material such as Paxolin. It has a matrix of holes, usually 0.1in pitch, with strips of copper on one side. Components mounted on the plain side of the board are interconnected by means of the copper track and the use of wire links. Beginners working with Veroboard often find difficulty in following the circuit which they have just constructed. This is because of the unusual configuration which is dictated by the copper tracks. In spite of these limitations, this type of construction is very useful to the constructor/experimenter as the method allows for modifications to be made and the final result is sufficiently stable to make a permanent job. The method is not to be recommended for radio frequencies above 5MHz due to the proximity of the parallel strips.

Fig 1.1 shows the arrangement of the holes and the copper strips. A simple project is described in Chapter 3 to give some experience in the use of Veroboard.

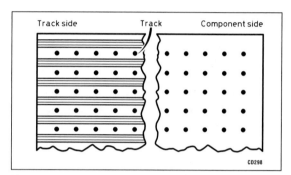

Fig 1.1. Veroboard

Prototype boards

These allow circuits to be set up in a temporary way for experimentation and development. No soldering is required and the components remain in good condition so that they can be used in the final circuit or elsewhere. There are a number of different types from which to choose. Table 1.1 lists some of them and gives comparative data. All are basically similar, with a plastic surface carrying a matrix of holes which have a series of interconnected sockets beneath. A wide variety of components can be plugged into these holes, and the interconnections allow circuits to be built up with the occasional use of short pieces of tinned copper wire to

Table 1.1. Details of some of the prototype boards currently available

Type	Number of sockets	Extras	Sources
Professional	550	—	Maplin, RS Components
	80	Extra busbars, component bracket	Maplin, RS Components
Euro	600	—	Maplin
Vero Block	360	—	Maplin
Multi-board *	840	—	Maplin

* Made up from four strips which suit many different spacings.

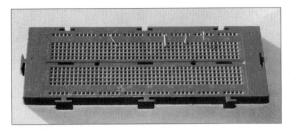

A typical prototype board

connect some strips together. Most boards use a 0.1 × 0.1in matrix with two groups of sockets separated by 0.3in which is the standard spacing for the pins of 8, 14 and 16-pin DIL (dual-in-line) integrated circuit packages.

A section of a typical board is shown in Fig 1.2. It will be seen that the main blocks are arranged in groups of five interconnected sockets. There are long rows of sockets at the top and bottom edges of the board which make very useful supply busbars. All decks have similar maximum ratings which allow for up to 50V between adjacent strips and a current of 1A per strip. *The mains electricity supply must never be connected to the board in any way.* Boards may usually be joined together to provide a greater working area. The type illustrated in the photograph comes complete with a support bracket which can be fitted into any one of three positions and allows normal panel components to be mounted. A strip having two extra busbars is also available. This will slot into the main board and simplifies the power supply arrangements when a number of different voltage rails are required.

Most boards have a system of alphanumeric labelling which allows any socket to be referred to in records or notes. In order to set up the circuit in an orderly fashion, considerable use of wire links is required; off-cuts from resistors and capacitors are very useful and the longer pieces should be saved for this purpose.

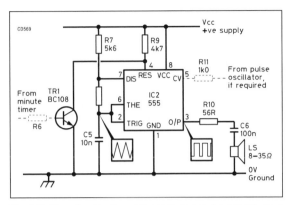

Fig 1.3. The circuit of an AF oscillator to be set up on a prototype board

The method of use is reasonably straightforward and is illustrated in Fig 1.3 which shows a simple circuit using an integrated circuit (555) as an AF oscillator. The practical layout of the components on a prototype board is shown in Fig 1.4. More information on this technique and a simple project is to be found in the November 1991 issue of the RSGB's journal *Radio Communication*.

This type of construction is not suitable for permanent circuits and should only be used for testing out a simple circuit or small sections of a larger one. As with Veroboard, the use of this method should be limited to frequencies of less than 5MHz.

Tag or terminal strip: point-to-point wiring

A rather old-fashioned way of making up a project – once all electronic circuits were built that way! For the beginner to home construction the method has some attraction. If electrical terminal strips are used the components can be fixed by means of the terminal screws, thus taking away the need for the soldering iron. This is the method used with the simple medium-wave radio recommended

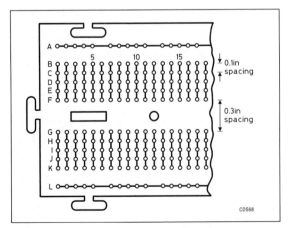

Fig 1.2. Section of a typical prototype board

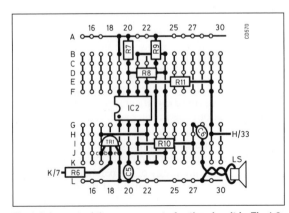

Fig 1.4. Layout of the components for the circuit in Fig 1.3

for trainee Novices. Fig 1.5 shows how most of the components in this design are fixed to an electrical terminal strip. The details of the complete radio receiver can be found in the RSGB publication *Novice Licence Student's Notebook*, and in the pilot issue of *D-i-Y Radio*. Tag strips use the same basic technique but the connections need to be soldered.

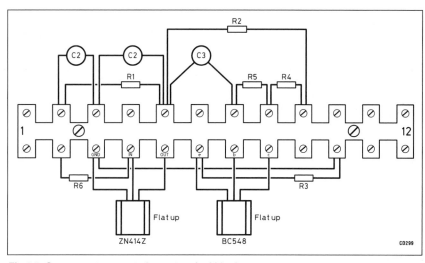

Fig 1.5. Components mounted on a terminal block

'Islands' on plain copper laminate – the 'ugly' method

This is the method which will be adopted for some of the projects described later. Small pieces of copper laminate board are glued to a larger piece of board so as to produce copper 'islands' on the main board. The copper side of the island is thus insulated from the main board which is given various names such as the 'motherboard' or the 'ground plane'. These terms will be explained later.

The wire ends of components are soldered to the 'islands' which are placed in position convenient for the size of the component and the circuit being produced. Fig 1.6 shows a simple project to be described in Chapter 3. Quite complex circuits can be wired by this method and by carefully placing the 'islands' the interconnections can be reduced to a minimum. Circuits will work satisfactorily up to 50MHz or more and it is very easy to make alterations to the circuit. Earth or chassis connections are usually made by soldering directly to the copper of the ground plane. Again, reference to Fig 1.6 will make this clear. If the 'islands' are fixed using the type of adhesive known as 'repositionable' it is easy to move them to a new position to allow for a new piece of circuitry. For a permanent circuit, 'superglue' or similar should be used.

The resulting circuit is rather untidy and it is from this that the name 'ugly' is derived.

An alternative is sometimes used – the components themselves are glued directly to the ground plane. Resistors and capacitors and other similar components are glued to the baseboard and the lead-out wires used as terminals which are joined together either by means of their own leads or by extra pieces of wire. Components such as transistors are glued to the board so that the leads are sticking up. The same method is adopted with integrated circuits. This gives rise to the name sometimes

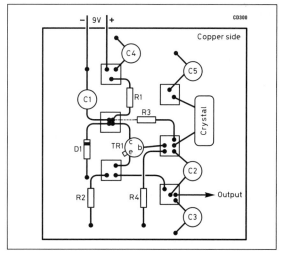

Fig 1.6. Components mounted on 'islands' on copper laminate

used to describe this method: 'dead bug construction'. Stand an IC on its back and you will see why.

Although this method of construction does not look very nice, it is an excellent way of setting up a circuit which can be made to operate up to quite high radio frequencies. 50MHz or more is easily obtainable and, if care is taken to fix the components securely, the circuit should be quite stable both mechanically and electrically. More information is given about about stability later. The other advantage of this method of construction is the ease with which the circuit can be followed at a later date and modified if necessary.

Chapter 2

How to make an RF probe and an absorption wavemeter

Building an oscillator or a transmitter can be relatively easy but, having built it, we need to know a number of things about it. Does it work at all? Is it providing the correct frequency signal? Is the output voltage or power correct? These questions and many others will arise when the project nears completion. Professionals and advanced constructors will have sophisticated equipment with which to check these points but the new constructor will probably not possess anything more than a meter.

RF probe

If you have a digital voltmeter (DVM), an RF probe will enable you to measure small radio frequency voltages. It may work with an analogue meter but it depends on the sensitivity. If your meter has a sensitivity of $20,000\Omega$ per volt or higher and a DC voltage range of 3V or less it will work quite well. The probe is a simple rectifying device which converts the RF into DC, which is then measured by the DVM set to a low-voltage DC range. You may quite correctly enquire why the meter is not set to an AC range. The answer is that the losses at RF (due to the capacitance of the leads and instrument) is high and little or none of the voltage under test will reach the DVM. The RF can 'pass through' a capacitor or any circuit which has capacitance. The probe overcomes this by rectifying the RF literally at the tip of the probe and so the losses are almost nil.

Circuit

The circuit shown in Fig 2.1 is very simple, consisting of two RF diodes which form a voltage-doubling rectifier

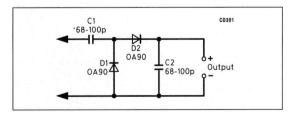

Fig 2.1. The circuit of the RF probe

Table 2.1. RF probe components list

C1, 2	68pF polystyrene
D1, 2	OA90 germanium point-contact diode
Plastic knitting needle 2.0mm diameter	
Brass or copper rod 1.5mm diameter, 35mm long	
Disused plastic pen barrel	
Banana plugs to suit meter: one red, one black	
Red and black PVC-coated wire	

circuit and two capacitors. The second, C2, removes most of the RF and presents a DC voltage to the DVM.

Construction

This is a variation on the 'ugly' method. Although it is not essential, the device is more convenient to use if it is fitted into a thin hollow tube. The prototype was built on a plastic knitting needle about 2mm in diameter. Anything thicker will make it very difficult to fit the assembly into a pen body, which is the container used in the probe to be described. A components list is given in Table 2.1.

1. The point of the probe can be made from a piece of brass or copper wire about 1.5mm in diameter and 35mm long. Bend it into the form of a very shallow 'Z', bind it to the end of the needle and then glue it. The bend 'offset' should be arranged so that the point and the needle are in approximate alignment to make it easier to fit the whole assembly into a pen barrel.

2. The components are arranged in two lines along the needle as shown in Fig 2.2. The polarity of the two diodes is most important: refer to the diagram. The cathode marks (a band) *must* be as shown. If the capacitors have a band or the letters 'OF' (standing for 'outside foil'), they should also be connected as shown, although the device will still work correctly if these are reversed.

3. Push the needle complete with components into the body of a disused ballpoint pen (the fatter variety) so that the tip of the wire protrudes by about 4mm. Fig 2.2 should make this clear. If the components listed have been used it should be possible to do this

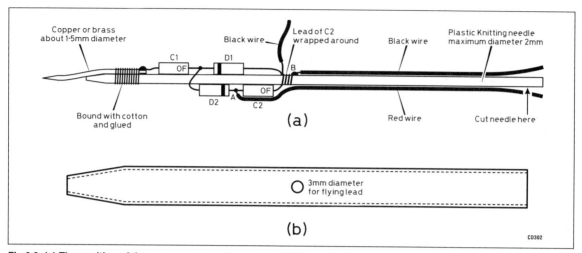

Fig 2.2. (a) The position of the components on the needle. (b) The pen body

successfully. Try to keep the leads of the components short but remember that germanium point-contact diodes can be damaged by too much heat, so make your joints quickly.

4. When everything fits into the body of the pen, carefully remove it, hold the assembly against the pen body and mark the position of the earth band of wire produced by wrapping the lead of C2 around the needle.

5. Make a 3mm hole in the plastic pen body at the position marked, pass a piece of PVC-insulated wire through the hole so that it comes out of the big end of the pen, and solder the wire to the earth band. Refer to Fig 2.2(a).

6. Solder the lead-out wires, red to point A and black to point B (the earth band). These wires can be twisted together or a piece of screened wire could be used.

7. Again hold the assembly up to the pen and mark the needle at the end of the pen barrel. Cut the needle at this point. If you are sure that all is in order, you can apply a tiny drop of superglue to the side of the four components to hold everything in position.

8. Gently push the complete assembly into the pen, while carefully pulling the lead coming out of the hole to take up the slack.

9. Finish off by fitting a red 4mm plug (or whatever size fits the sockets on your meter) to the red lead and a black one to the black lead.

10. Finally, solder a small crocodile clip to the flying lead coming from the middle of the body.

The probe can be used in 'chassis' form provided that the components are not touched, but the pen will make it easier to use and make it look good.

Using the probe

When using this test device, it must be remembered that it is almost unaffected by the frequency of the RF and

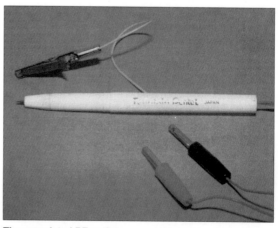

The probe removed from the pen body

The completed RF probe

simply indicates that there is an RF voltage present. If there is more than one signal present the probe can give no indication of this; the output voltage will simply be a function of all input signals. As the probe uses a voltage doubler and because the meter connected to the output draws almost no current, the voltage at the output will be almost equal to the peak-to-peak voltage of the RF input, that is twice the peak voltage and approximately three times the RMS value.

In use the crocodile clip is normally connected to the 'earthy' end (usually 0V) and the point of the probe to the part of the circuit to be tested. More about this later.

A different method of measurement must be used to obtain some idea of the frequency of the input signal and to select one signal only. This can be both an advantage and a disadvantage. The probe will work at almost any radio frequency whereas a frequency-measuring device will only work within the range of the design.

An absorption wavemeter

This is actually a crystal radio receiver with a meter in place of a telephone earpiece. The choice of meter is most important: one having a low sensitivity will not work. Try to find a meter with a full-scale deflection current (FSD) of less than 250µA. A lower FSD will provide a more sensitive wavemeter, or in other words it will respond to weaker signals. The meter quoted in the parts list represents the type which can be bought new for about £2.50 but second-hand meters can often be found at radio rallies.

Circuit

Fig 2.3 shows the circuit of the wavemeter to be built. It works in the same way as the RF probe except that it has a tuned circuit which must be adjusted to the frequency of the transmitter or oscillator under test. The signal from the transmitter is rectified by the two diodes, which again act as a voltage-doubling rectifier, and the resulting DC voltage is measured by the meter. The coil L1 and L2 and the variable capacitor VC1 can be tuned to a variety of frequencies and with the values shown all frequencies between 3.5 and 8MHz will be covered. When only L1 is used with VC1 the frequency will be from about 9MHz to 30MHz. This will enable all amateur HF bands to be accepted with the exception of Top Band which covers 1.8 to 2.0MHz.

It is not really necessary for the device to work on this band because it is normally used to detect harmonics of the band in use and those from a transmitter operating in Top Band will fall in the range mentioned above. However, if it is felt necessary to cover Top Band, a simple modification will allow these frequencies to be received although it might be advisable to make a separate wavemeter for this band. The only difference is in the coil

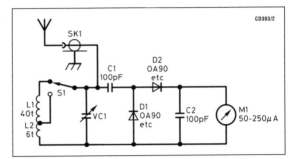

Fig 2.3. The circuit of the absorption wavemeter. D1 and D2 are OA90, OA91, OA95 or similar

and/or capacitor. Constructors keen enough to get the device working on Top Band could experiment with different values of capacitor connected in parallel with VC1. A value in the range 150 to 220pF should be about right.

If VC1 is calibrated, the device will give an idea of the frequency of the received signal. Later on we will use the circuit to test the output of a transmitter to see if it is producing unwanted harmonic frequencies. More about these later. It will also be helpful in the setting-up process of the 50MHz FM transmitter to be described later.

Construction

Note that if a variable capacitor other than the one mentioned in the components list (Table 2.2) is used, it must have the same maximum capacitance (140pF) or the number of turns on L1 and L2 will have to be modified. If screws are to be used to fix VC1 they should be M2.5 and the length no more than 3mm. (This assumes a panel thickness of 1–1.5mm.) Read the text on p13 of Chapter 3 which gives details of the process. If you cannot obtain screws of this short length, refer to Appendix 1.

1. To make L1, obtain a former having a diameter of about 15mm and made of wood or plastic. Wind 40 turns of 0.4mm enamel-covered wire in a single layer on the former with the turns touching one another. Start the winding about 15mm from one end of the former, leaving about 30mm for the connection to the rest of the circuit. The turns can be held in position by means of candle wax which is carefully melted

Table 2.2. Wavemeter components list

C1, 2	100pF polystyrene
VC1	Miniature variable capacitor. Maplin type FT78K with 6mm spindle extension piece and screw
D1, 2	OA90, OA91, OA95 or any germanium point-contact diode
SK1	Phono socket. Maplin type YW06G or similar
S1	Single-pole double-throw (SPDT) switch
M1	50–250µA meter. Maplin type LB80B (see text)

Two M2.5 (3mm long) fixing screws for VC1 (see Appendix 1)
About 6m of 0.4mm enamel-covered wire

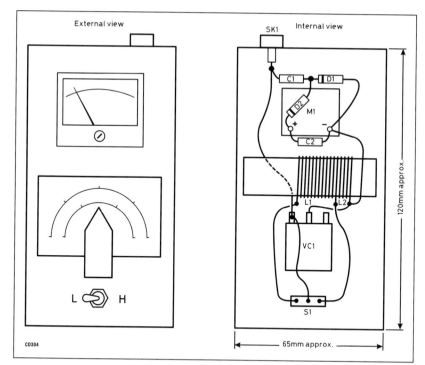

Fig 2.4. Suggested layout for the components

drawn on it with a hole in the centre to allow the spindle of VC1 to pass through.

7. Glue the card to the box and then fit the control knob.

Calibration

This can be difficult for the beginner and is best left until some of the oscillator and transmitter projects are completed. A friendly amateur with an HF transceiver could make the operation easy by tuning the transmitter to a few spot frequencies.

If the crystal oscillator described in Chapter 3 has been completed, the first calibration mark could be made using it.

1. Connect a short piece of wire to the input socket of the wavemeter and lay it close to the oscillator.

2. Move the tuning capacitor VC1 slowly through its range and watch the meter for a deflection. If none occurs, move S1 to the other position and try again. If there is still no response move the input wire closer to the oscillator and repeat the process.

3. When an indication is obtained, adjust the tuning control for maximum deflection on the meter and then carefully mark the position of the control on the dial. This will correspond to a frequency of 3.579MHz as that is the frequency of the crystal used in the oscillator.

4. At the same time mark the position of the switch with the word 'LOW' and the other position 'HIGH'.

Calibration does not need to be extremely accurate – marks on the dial for each of the amateur bands are usually all that is required. The wavemeter should not be thought of as a frequency-measuring device but rather as one which gives an idea of the frequency under test. For accurate measurement a digital frequency meter would normally be used. One of these can measure frequencies with an accuracy of less than one hertz. It would be helpful if you can find an amateur who has such a device and may be prepared to measure the output frequencies of some of your projects.

Note that this little test meter does not need any power supply other than that which comes from the oscillator under test. Any circuit which works in this way is called a 'passive' device.

Other wavemeters are described in later chapters when they are required for testing or setting up.

with the bit of a hot soldering iron. The task is made even easier if a piece of double-sided sticky tape about 25mm wide is wrapped around the former before the wire is wound on. The tape will hold the turns until they are held permanently by the candle wax.

2. Remove the enamel insulation from the inside ends of both L1 and L2. This can be done with a sharp knife used with a scraping action. The operation is made easier if the wire is heated in the flame from a match for a few moments.

3. Twist the bare ends together to form the tap in the coil and solder.

4. Assemble the wavemeter into a small plastic box. Size is not important as long as it is big enough to contain the coil former. The layout is shown in Fig 2.4 but this can be modified to suit the box in use. Fix the coil former by means of glue or double-sided sticky pads.

5. Mount the phono socket, tuning capacitor C1 and switch S1 in the box once suitable holes have been made in it. The material is quite soft and holes can be drilled and filed with a round file to the required size. If a taper reamer is available it is even easier but take care to avoid too much pressure on the reamer as it is very easy to make the holes too big.

6. Make a simple dial for the tuning control. This can be a piece of thick white paper with two semicircles

Chapter 3

Some simple oscillators

First let's review some theory. An oscillator is an amplifier which provides an input from its own output, but what is an amplifier?

This analogy should help. A slide projector uses light from a lamp, probably operated from the mains, to make a big copy of the picture contained on the slide. If the lenses are good then the picture projected on to the screen will differ from the one on the slide in size only. Note that the picture we see is not the original on the slide but just a big copy of it.

An electronic amplifier works in very much the same way. It uses electrical energy (from a battery or from the mains) to make a big copy of a varying voltage which is applied to its input. Again note that the input signal is not made bigger but the circuit makes a big copy. If the amplifier is 'linear', that is, it does not cause distortion, then the only difference between the input and output signals is one of size.

In an oscillator the input is provided by the output of the amplifier and if the losses in the circuit are not too great a continuous signal will be provided.

Let's look at the function another way. If a coil and capacitor are connected in parallel and energy is put into the capacitor, that energy will be transferred to the coil and back from the coil into the capacitor. The action will continue until all of the original energy has been lost in the form of heat in the circuit. It is just like the action of a swing or pendulum – give it a push (put energy in) and it will swing (oscillate) until all of the energy has been lost – again in the form of heat. In both cases we could arrange for energy to be put into the circuit automatically to make up for the losses. A swing can be pushed at the right moment in time and the circuit could have energy put in by the use of an amplifier.

The simple circuit shown in Fig 3.1 works in that way. The two resistors R1 and R2 bias the transistor so that it conducts when the supply is connected. C2 modifies the bias once the circuit is oscillating. When the supply is switched on current from the battery flows through L2 and the magnetic field produced induces a voltage in L1. Some of this voltage is applied to the input of the amplifier

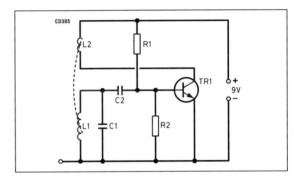

Fig 3.1. A simple oscillator

(the transistor), causing the collector current to vary at the same frequency as the oscillation taking place in L1/C1. This varying current flowing through L2 puts energy into L1 at the correct moment in time and keeps the oscillation going. As with the swing, the direction of the push must be right – if it comes from the wrong side, the swing will stop, so the connections to L1 and L2 must be correct so that the energy from the battery helps the energy already in the circuit.

There are other circuits in addition to the coil and capacitor which will act as oscillators. An important one is the quartz crystal. For the time being, think of the crystal as another tuned circuit just like L1/C1 in the circuit above.

A fixed-frequency (crystal) oscillator

Fig 3.2 shows the circuit of a very simple crystal oscillator. If you have never made an RF oscillator before, this will make a good introductory project.

The diode D1 and the resistor R1 are not essential to the operation of the oscillator but it is good practice to feed a crystal oscillator (or any other type) from a stable voltage in order to prevent changes in frequency when the supply voltage alters. D1 is a zener diode which keeps the voltage across it almost constant in spite of any change in battery voltage etc.

Later, in the chapters dealing with microwave projects,

you will find that the effect of voltage change is put to good use to provide frequency modulation. Much more about this later.

Look at the layout diagram in Fig 3.3 and note that the type of construction to be used is the 'ugly' method – small 'islands' of copper laminate on a sheet of similar material. Try to see how the practical circuit compares with the theoretical one.

The materials required are quite easily obtainable and apart from the crystal can be bought for a few pence. A components list is given in Table 3.1.

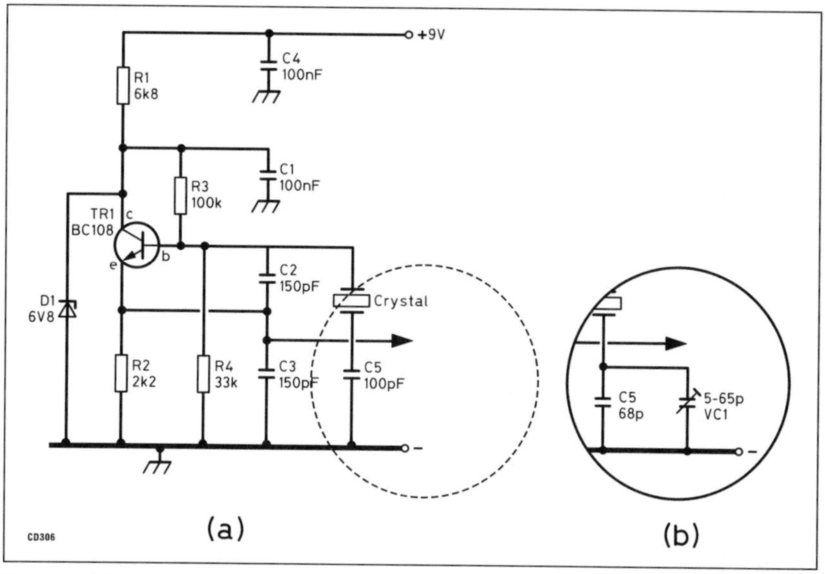

Checking components

If you have a test meter (you will need one if you intend to progress very far into this book), you can check the components as part of the construction process.

Measure the value of each resistor and check it corresponds with its markings.

The resistance of capacitors should be infinite (∞) on the ohms scale. For future reference, larger-capacitance capacitors will show a movement of the pointer towards zero with a very rapid fall back to ∞. Electrolytic capacitors will cause a large flick of the pointer and may show some finite resistance when the pointer comes to rest. Note that the positively polarised lead of the meter (not necessarily the positive or '+' one) must be connected to the positive lead of the capacitor.

Transistors can be checked by using the simple circuit shown in Fig 3.4. First we must find out the polarity of the meter leads when it is in the resistance mode. There are a number of ways of doing this but the method indicated in Fig 3.4(a) and (b) is very simple and foolproof. Switch the meter to the lowest ohms range. Connect a capacitor with a capacitance of 100nF or more to the meter

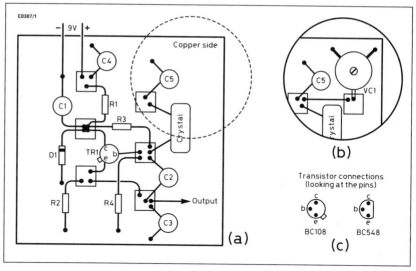

Fig 3.2. (a) The circuit of a practical crystal oscillator. (b) Modification to allow setting to a precise frequency

Fig 3.3. (a) The component layout of the oscillator. (b) Modification to allow setting to a precise frequency. (c) Transistor connections

leads. As the connection is made you will see a flick of the meter needle – this is not important at this stage except that it indicates that you have used a good capacitor. Remove the meter leads from the capacitor but do not touch the capacitor wires. Switch the meter to a low DC volts range and connect the meter leads to the capacitor once more. Watch the pointer carefully. If it flicks forward then the polarity of the meter when in the resistance mode is as the meter is marked. That is, the positive

Table 3.1. Components list for the crystal oscillator

RESISTORS
R1	6k8
R2	2k2
R3	100k
R4	33k

CAPACITORS
C1, 3	100n polyester
C2, 4	150p mica

MISCELLANEOUS
TR1	BC108 or equivalent
D1	Miniature 6.8V zener diode
X1	3.579MHz (or any low-price crystal in the 80m band)

Pieces of copper laminate – 50 × 50mm and 5 × 5mm

Note: component values in circuit diagrams and most lists in this book are given with the multiplier replacing the decimal point, so for, say, resistors, 820R = 820Ω, 2k2 = 2.2kΩ, 3M9 = 3.9MΩ etc. Similarly, for capacitors, 150p = 150pF.

lead is positive but if the pointer tries to move backwards (to the left of zero) then the polarity of the meter is reversed.

Another method involves using a diode. Switch the meter to a low ohms range, connect it across the diode

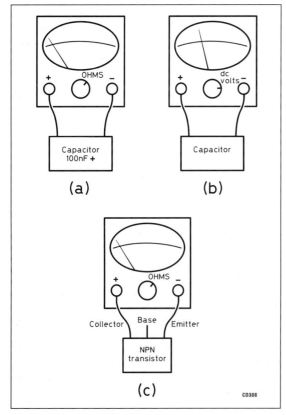

Fig 3.4. A simple test for transistors

with the negative lead of the meter to the cathode of the diode (indicated by a band at one end of the package). The resistance will be infinity (∞) if the polarity of the meter is reversed when in the resistance mode, and about 1000 to 2000Ω if the polarity remains the same. Having checked your meter, remember the polarity when switched to measure ohms – it will not change!

To test an NPN transistor, switch the meter to a low ohms range. Connect the collector to the positively polarised terminal of the meter and the emitter to the negatively polarised terminal. The indication should be infinity (∞). Damp your finger and touch both the base and the collector lead at the same time but without allowing the two leads to touch one another. The meter should now register some resistance value. If you prefer, a 47kΩ resistor may be used in the place of a wet finger. This is a bit more fiddly and the author always uses a wet finger. If no deflection of the meter pointer occurs, try the next higher range. If there is still no indication the transistor is almost certainly faulty or is not an NPN type.

A PNP type is tested in the same way except that the collector is connected to the negative terminal of the meter and the emitter to the positive. The remainder of the test is as before.

Construction

1. First prepare the motherboard. This is a piece of single- or double-sided copper laminate board about 50 × 50mm square. If the surface of the copper is bright and clean it can be used without any treatment but if it is dirty or tarnished it must be cleaned at this stage. Fine wire wool used dry will be satisfactory or there are special cleaning blocks available. These are rather like the old fashioned 'ink eraser' which cleans without scratching. If there is nothing else suitable, a scouring pad with a little detergent will be OK but the board must be dried thoroughly with clean tissue before proceeding.

2. Another piece of copper laminate should be cleaned in the same way.

3. Using a ballpoint pen or a compass point, mark a line about 5mm from one edge on this second piece of copper laminate and with a fine saw carefully cut off the strip (or use the technique described in Appendix 1).

4. Use a fine file to remove the sharp edges and then cut the strip into squares. About six to eight will be needed to complete the oscillator. Try to avoid touching them too much as fingermarks will make soldering difficult.

5. Examine the components and identify each one.

6. If you have a test meter, check the value of each of the resistors is as marked.

7. If you have a test meter, check that the capacitors are

not showing any leakage as described in the previous section.

8. If you have a test meter, check the transistors as described in the previous section.

9. When all components are identified lay them out with the small square 'islands' onto the motherboard. It is better to attempt to do this by looking at the circuit diagram only; this is good practice for future projects. However, if you have trouble, refer to the layout diagram shown in Fig 3.3.

10. When you are satisfied that everything will fit, draw around each 'island' with a sharp pencil.

11. Remove the components and cement the 'islands' in the marked position with the copper side facing up. Remember that if you feel you will need to move the 'islands' to a new position later, a repositionable-type adhesive must be used. Most shops selling drawing equipment will be able to supply this and other types of adhesives. It is advisable for the early stages of a project – a more-permanent type such as superglue can be used for the finished product.

12. Start with R1. Bend the leads though 90°, close to the body, and then make a second bend about 5mm away from the first so as to make a 'foot'. One of the problems with this form of construction is the tendency for the old connection to collapse as a new one is made to the same 'island'. The 'foot' helps to avoid this as the wires will lie over one another. For the same reason, allow the solder to 'set' on one island before moving on to the next.

13. Place the resistor in position across the appropriate pads and use the soldering iron to flow solder over the surface of the 'island'. Keep the component still until the solder has set, then solder the other end. The wire ends can be clipped off before or after soldering, whichever is easier.

14. Next solder C2 but note that the lead connecting it to C3 is not clipped off but bent instead so that it makes a bridge to the junction of R2 and the emitter of the transistor.

15. Solder one end of R2 to its 'island' but the other to the motherboard. All chassis or ground connections are made in this way, giving rise to the name 'ground plane'.

16. Continue with R3 and R4, which also have one lead soldered to the ground plane.

17. Follow with the other four capacitors and the crystal, all of which have the leads bent in the same way so that all of the components are standing up on the motherboard by a few millimetres.

18. Solder in the diode D1. This component must be connected with the correct polarity. Note the band at one end of the diode, and fix as shown in Fig 3.3.

19. Finally, solder in the transistor. This has three wires and care must be taken to ensure that they are connected exactly as shown. Two different types of transistor package are shown and the arrangement for each type is indicated in the layout diagram Fig 3.3.

Testing the oscillator

The construction is complete and the oscillator can now be tested. If you have already made the diode probe described in Chapter 2, proceed as follows.

1. Connect the positive lead of the probe to the positive terminal of the DVM (or the analogue meter if suitable), which should be set to the lowest DC range unless the instrument is of the type known as 'autoranging'.

2. Connect the negative lead of the probe to the negative terminal of the DVM.

3. Connect a suitable supply to the oscillator: a 9V battery such as a PP3 or 9V from a power supply unit.

4. Connect the crocodile clip on the flying lead from the probe to the ground plane of the motherboard.

5. Apply the point of the probe to the point marked 'Output'; this can be the 'island' which links C1, C2, R2 and the transistor together. An indication in the region of 1.0V should be obtained. If no output occurs check the connections of the circuit with special attention to those of the transistor.

If you have any other crystals with frequencies in the ranges 1.950 to 2.000MHz or 3.565 to 3.585MHz they could be used instead of the one specified. No other circuit changes are necessary.

The friendly amateur with a digital frequency meter could be very helpful at this stage to let you convince yourself of the frequency of the oscillator but don't go to too much trouble to find one; there are other ways of 'measuring' the frequency. The absorption meter described in Chapter 2 would be suitable when it has been calibrated! A radio receiver that covers Top Band will pick up the signal from the oscillator if its antenna is held very close to the project board.

As this is an experimental project, you could try a modification which involves replacing C5 with a capacitor having a value of 68pF and connecting a miniature variable capacitor (VC1) in parallel with it as shown in Fig 3.2(b). There is enough room on the board to allow for this. VC1 can be varied from 5 to 65pF, allowing the frequency of the oscillator to be 'pulled' away from its original frequency by a few hundred hertz. The variable capacitor enables the oscillator to be set to a precise frequency in the range of the declared crystal frequency ±200 to 300Hz.

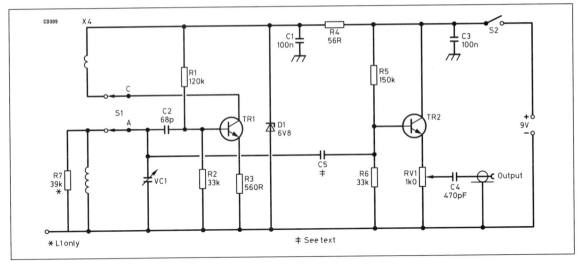

Fig 3.5. The circuit diagram of the simple signal generator

A variable frequency oscillator

This is a little more complicated than the crystal oscillator. However, as it is possible to change the frequency of oscillation to any value in the range 1.780 to 30.000MHz, it can act as a simple signal generator which, if calibrated carefully, can be used to check the operation of receivers which have been constructed or repaired. It is possible to cover the whole of this range in one instrument but some rather elaborate switching is required. To simplify the design, a number of frequency range options are suggested and it is recommended that the one thought to be most useful be attempted first. The major difference is in the choice of coil; almost all of the remaining components are the same in each option. The construction is the same in each case, and the design is such that the other options can be added later.

If only one of the suggested ranges is required, only one coil will be used and no switching is necessary. Two ranges will require two coils and a simple switch, three ranges will use three coils and all four will need four coils – the switching then gets a little complicated.

The circuit diagram is shown in Fig 3.5 and it is worthwhile trying to follow it, although the project can be built without reference to the circuit.

The construction described allows the simplest option to be attempted first and then as experience in working in limited space is gained it will be possible to move up to two or more ranges.

With a frequency range as above it must be clear that this oscillator can generate signals outside those allocated to amateur radio and the design must ensure that the radiation is kept to a very low level. Changes in component type may be made but the physical construction must

be followed as it forms the screening necessary to prevent any excessive radiation.

Table 3.2. Components list for the signal generator

RESISTORS
R1	120k
R2, 6	33k
R3	560R
R4	56R
R5	150k
R7	39k

All resistors are 0.5W carbon film.
RV1   1k miniature horizontal pot (Maplin JM69A)

CAPACITORS
C1, 3	100n polyester
C2	68p ceramic or silver mica
C4	470p ceramic or silver mica
C5	Home-made – see text
VC1	140/60p AM/FM miniature tuning type (Maplin FT78K)

SEMICONDUCTORS
TR1, 2   BC548 or BC108
D1   6.8V zener diode – any miniature type

INDUCTORS
L1	TOKO KANK3333R (Maplin FD02C or Cirkit 35-33330)
L2	TOKO 154AN7A6440E (Cirkit 35-64400)
L3	TOKO KANK3334R (Maplin FD03D or Cirkit 35-33340)
L4	TOKO KANK3335R (Maplin FD04E or Cirkit 35-33350)

MISCELLANEOUS
S1	2-pole 6-way rotary (Maplin FF74R or Cirkit 53-21024)
S2	SPDT miniature toggle (Maplin FH00A or Cirkit 53-00200)

Output socket, single-hole phono (Maplin YW06G)
Battery clip for PP3
Slow-motion drive, epicyclic ball drive (Maplin RK42V)
3 suitable knobs
Copper laminate
Several 6BA or M2.5 screws with nuts

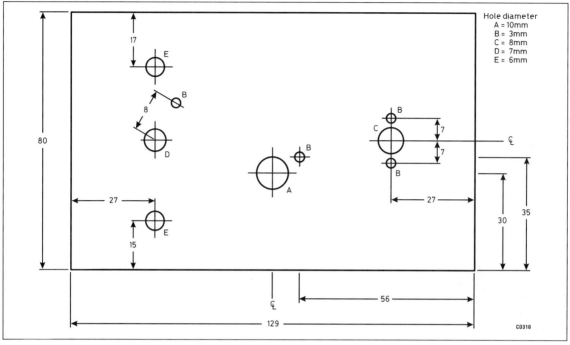

Fig 3.6. The drilling detail for the panel

The construction method used is again the 'ugly' method with the addition of an internal box made up by soldering pieces of copper laminate board together. It is worth mentioning here that one of the disadvantages of the 'ugly' method of construction is that the circuit is not laid out as it would be with a printed circuit.

A components list for this project is given in Table 3.2.

Constructing the internal box

This is actually easier than it sounds. If you have any doubts, practice with a few odd scraps of material before attempting the final job. The secret is to get the edges as straight as possible. This will be easier if the edge of the piece of copper laminate is rubbed along a fine file which is laid flat on the work surface. A big file is easier to use than a small one because it will not slide about as the piece of board is rubbed along it. If you are tempted to hold the file in a vice, don't tighten the jaws of the vice too much because files are rather brittle and may snap, leaving some unpleasant, sharp edges.

When making the sides for a box it will be easier to cut a piece which is long enough to make all sides. For example, if a box having an inside measurement of 50 × 40mm by 35mm deep is to be made, cut a piece of sheet 190 × 35mm. This will cut up into two pieces 50 × 35mm and two 40 × 35mm but use the technique just described before cutting to get the edge straight. It is much easier to handle a long piece rather than four short ones, and all

the pieces are more likely to be of the same 'height'. This is most important if the top of the finished box is to be soldered to a flat sheet.

Use a large bit in the soldering iron, hold the two pieces in position and solder 2 to 3mm at one time. Allow to cool before moving on to the next section. Try making a small open-topped box by soldering the inside edges where the copper meets. Boxes of this type are very useful where extra radio frequency screening is required – any RF energy inside will not get out so easily. In other words, it will help to stop radiation.

Constructing the motherboard

When you have successfully made a box it is time to start work on the signal generator. The panel or motherboard is a piece of double-sided copper laminate cut and drilled using the dimensions in Fig 3.6. Look at the layout diagram in Fig 3.7. It is most important to know which component belongs to each of the holes. Great care must be taken with the position and size of the holes. Those marked 'B' are for fixing the tuning capacitor and 'C' is for its spindle. *The fixing holes must be exactly 14mm apart.* Drill a small hole first and make it larger by using a round needle file. Take care – it has a sharp point (don't stab yourself!) and it is very easily broken.

Using this method will allow the position of the holes to be changed and, by regularly holding the component in position as the work progresses, you should be able to see when the holes line up with those in the capacitor. When satisfied that the holes are correct, try the fixing screws. These are 2.5mm in diameter (called 'M2.5 screws') and *must not be more than 4mm long*. (This assumes a panel thickness of 1–1.5mm.) Anything longer will almost certainly cause a short-circuit to the vanes inside the capacitor. If it is necessary to shorten the screws refer to the section relating to screws in Appendix 1 for information on the correct method of doing this.

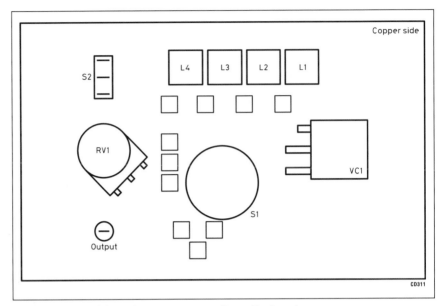

Fig 3.7. Position of the main components on the motherboard

Use your continuity tester or meter set to measure ohms to check that no short-circuit has occurred. Connect the tester between the copper of the motherboard on the component side and each of the two outside solder tags of the capacitor. If a short-circuit does occur, either (a) the screws must be shortened by putting on a nut, holding the nut in a vice and filing or (b) a small washer used under each screw head.

The remaining holes are not quite so critical but again check with the appropriate component as often as possible. Remember it is easy to make holes bigger but not smaller.

Modifying the switch

The holes marked 'B' for the locator spigot on the switch and the output control are given dimensions in Fig 3.6 but it is easier to find the correct position for these by removing the nut and washer from the component, putting it in position and twisting the control just a little so as to make a scuff mark on the copper. This enables the hole to be located accurately.

No components must be soldered to the board before you are sure that those to be mounted in the holes will fit correctly. It is very difficult to adjust them once components are soldered around their position.

Before the switch is finally fitted, the limit stop must be set so as to give the switch the correct number of positions ('ways'). The recommended switch is one which is known as '2-pole 6-way'. This indicates that it contains two switches, each with six positions. Fig 3.8 shows the arrangement. The project requires a switch with two internal switches with four positions, ie a '2-pole 4-way'

device, if all the ranges are to be set up eventually. The limit stop allows the switch to be modified to any state from 2-pole 2-way to 2-pole 6-way (as supplied). Modify the switch as follows.

1. Remove the nut and shakeproof washer from the switch. Another washer will probably fall out of position – this is the limit stop washer. If it doesn't

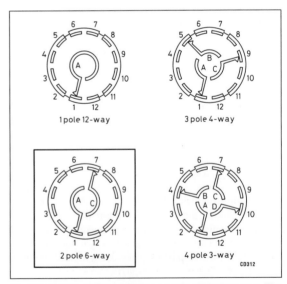

Fig 3.8. Some of the available switch arrangements. The diagram within the box shows the variation used in the project

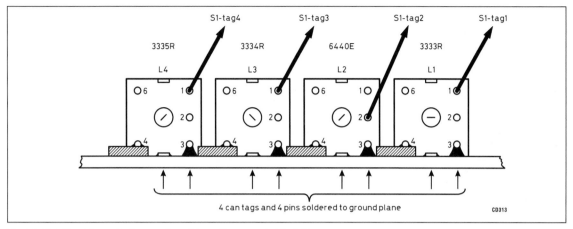

Fig 3.9. Details of the coil pins as viewed from the arrow in Fig 3.10

become loose, rotate the spindle of the switch. If it is still reluctant to leave its bed, help it out with an ordinary pin.

2. Hold the body of the switch firmly and turn the spindle anti-clockwise until it reaches a stop.

3. To give the switch four positions, replace the limit stop washer so that the tab goes into the slot marked '4'. (For three positions, into slot 3; for two positions, into slot 2).

4. Check that the operation has been carried out correctly – the switch should have only four positions.

5. Next use a continuity tester; any multimeter switched to a low-resistance range will do. Turn the spindle fully anti-clockwise. Test continuity between the centre tag marked 'A' and terminal 1 – the meter should indicate a short-circuit, that is, zero ohms. Similarly centre tag C to terminal 7 should be a short-circuit. There should not be any short-circuit between A or C and any of the other pins or between A and C.

6. Turn the spindle one step clockwise. Check A to 2 and C to 8; both should be a short-circuit.

7. Repeat by turning the spindle another step clockwise – check A to 3 and C to 9, and again expect a short-circuit.

8. Finally move the spindle to the last position. Check A to 4 and C to 10.

It is most important to have everything right before fitting the control to the motherboard. When you are sure that the switch is operating correctly, bend the four tags marked '5', '6', '11' and '12' towards the centre of the body just enough to remind you that they should not be used when connecting the other components.

Assembling the oscillator

1. Before fitting anything to the panel carefully mark the position of the ten 5 × 5mm 'islands'. An ordinary pencil will be satisfactory and the lines need not be removed. The four 'islands' along the top of the board must be positioned accurately.

2. When all are marked, temporarily fit the switch to ensure that the 'islands' are not covered by it.

3. Remove the switch and glue the 'islands' in position using superglue. It is easier to put a small spot of glue in the correct position on the board and to place the 'island' in position, making any adjustments to the position very quickly – the glue sets fast! Watch your fingers – superglue fixes them as well.

4. Fit the switch but make one more check that the limit stop has not moved.

5. Fit the tuning capacitor but remember that the screws must not be longer than 4mm.

6. Install the output control, output socket and on/off switch.

7. Fit the coils L1 to L4 as required. Each coil should be installed in the correct place, so that if range 2 is to be omitted the position for L2 will be left blank. This makes it very easy to add the other ranges later. Place the coil in position so that the tag on the can is against the board and the side having only two pins is on the left-hand side (with the board positioned with the coils at the top). Refer to Fig 3.9. The left-hand pin should rest on the 'island', with the can tag and right-hand pin clear of the next 'island' to the right. Very gently bend the right-hand pin so that it just touches the board. Solder the can tag and the right-hand pin to the motherboard and the left-hand pin to its 'island'. Refer to Fig 3.9. Repeat the process for each of the coils to be fitted, taking care to ensure that there is room for any coil not fitted to be put in later.

Refer to Fig 3.10 for steps 8 to 12.

8. Using bare tinned copper wire (about 22swg or 30A fuse wire) link the four 'islands' situated just below the coils.

9. Fit D1, observing the position of the cathode band.

10. Follow with the resistors R1, R2, R3 and R4, placing them as close as possible to the indicated position.

11. Fit C1 and C2.

12. Solder the centre tag of VC1 to the motherboard.

Refer to Fig 3.11 for steps 13 to 18 (the connections etc made in steps 8 to 12 have been omitted for the sake of clarity).

13. Again using tinned copper wire, link the switch contacts as follows. Tag 4 to L4 top right pin. Tag 3 to L3 top right pin. Tag 2 to L2 *middle* right pin and tag 1 to L1 top right-hand pin. The coil pin connections are shown in Fig 3.9.

14. Connect S1 tag A to VC1.

15. Fit R7.

16. Connect S1 tag C to the upper of the three 'islands' to the left of the switch.

17. Solder the tag of RV1 to the motherboard and the tag at the opposite end of RV1 to the left-hand 'island' around TR2.

18. Fit TR1 and TR2 carefully, observing the position of the 'flats' on the transistor body in each case.

Refer to Fig 3.12 for steps 19 to 24. Again, previous connections etc have been omitted from the diagram.

19. All the following connections with the exception of

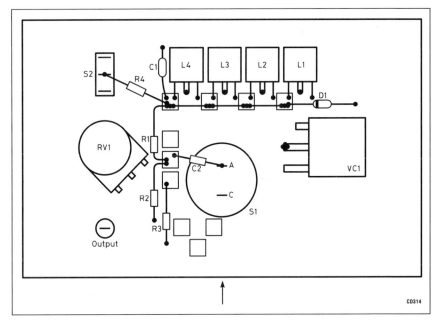

Fig 3.10. Components and wiring to be added in steps 8 to 12

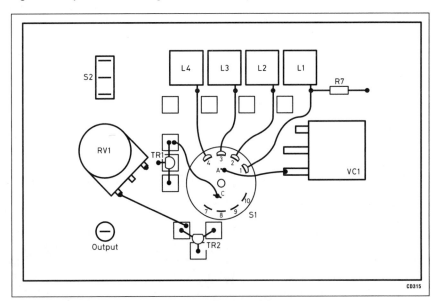

Fig 3.11. Components and wiring to be added in steps 13 to 18

that to C5 in step 24 are made using insulated wire. Link the four tags 7, 8, 9 and 10 on S1 to pin 6 (top left) of the coils L4, L3, L2 and L1 as shown. Refer to Fig 3.9 if necessary.

20. Fit R5 and R6.

21. Connect the centre tag on S2 to the 'island' just below S1.

22. Fit C3 and C4.

23. Connect the battery clip with the red lead going to the top tag of S2 and the black one soldered to the motherboard.

24. C5 needs to be a capacitor of very low value and the best way is to make it. Use a small piece of double-sided copper board 2mm square or less if you can handle it. A piece which is too big will feed too much signal to the base of TR2 on the low-frequency ranges, giving rise to a high harmonic content in the signal. Solder a length of tinned copper wire to the copper on one side and solder the other side of the square to the tag of VC1. Solder the wire to the 'island' connecting R5 and R6 together. Congratulations – the board is complete.

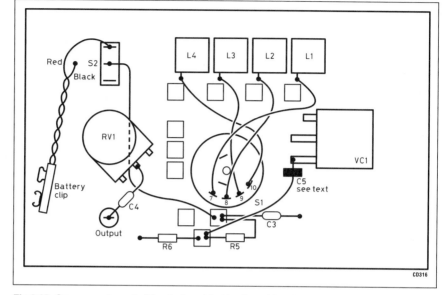

Fig 3.12. Components and wiring to be added in steps 19 to 24

Setting up

You may have to get some help to carry this out correctly but some idea of the way in which it works can be obtained by using the diode RF probe and/or the wavemeter.

1. Connect a 9V battery – the type known as 'PP3' is suitable but it would be advisable to use a rechargeable type if possible. The signal generator draws about 30mA so it could be rather expensive to use standard-type batteries. The extra cost of a rechargeable battery will soon be saved.

2. Set the 'Range' switch to position 1 and RV1 fully clockwise.

3. Connect the RF probe to the output socket and to the motherboard, set the meter to the 3V DC range and an output of about 1V should be obtained. It will almost certainly change as the tuning control is moved so the exact value is not important.

4. Move the range switch to position 2 and repeat. Then try positions 3 and 4. If you get a reading on all four ranges everything is working on some frequency.

5. Check the operation of RV1. The output should fall to zero with the control turned fully anti-clockwise.

6. In order to get the maximum frequency coverage on each band it is necessary to set the trimmers to minimum. Examine VC1 – there are two screws on the back and if these are turned by means of a small screwdriver it should be possible to see the moving vane of the trimmer. Set both the screws so that the vanes are not covering the fixed vanes. See Fig 3.13.

The completed VFO component board

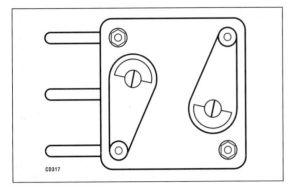

Fig 3.13. Showing the position of the trimmers for maximum frequency coverage

7. Checking the exact frequency is more difficult. If you have or can borrow a general-coverage receiver the ranges can be calibrated. Put the range switch to position 1 and set the receiver to 2MHz in a CW mode. Rotate the tuning control of the signal generator slowly and a whistle should be heard at some point.

8. By repeating this operation at a number of different frequencies the coverage of range 1 can be determined. Set the receiver to 1.78MHz and the control of the signal generator fully anti-clockwise. Using a proper trimming tool, adjust the iron core of L1 until a whistle is heard from the receiver.

9. Repeat the process for position 2 of the range switch but this time tune the receiver to 3.2MHz and adjust the core of L2 for a whistle.

10. Repeat twice more using positions 3 and 4 of the range switch and receiver frequencies of 6.4 and 13.0MHz respectively.

The coverage of each range should be in the region of:

Range 1 – 1.78 to 4.9MHz
Range 2 – 3.15 to 6.95MHz
Range 3 – 6.35 to 18.3MHz
Range 4 – 12.9 to 31.0MHz

If you intend to build a generator with restricted coverage the above table will enable you to decide which ranges to install.

Building the screening box

1. Double-sided copper board should be used. Cut five pieces with the following dimensions in millimetres: one 100×70, two 103×25 and two 70×25.

2. The two copper surfaces of the longer sides and the top need to be connected together. Drill two 1mm holes in each piece, pass a piece of tinned copper wire through the holes, bend the end over and solder.

3. Cut the other end of the wire so that it sticks out about 2mm, bend it over and again solder. Do this in at least two positions in each long side. If you do not have any 1mm drills, make two short cuts on one of the long sides (about 2mm deep) using a junior hacksaw, put the tinned copper wire through the slot and solder both sides. This 'plating through' operation is necessary to ensure that all of the surface of the box is connected to the ground plane when it is finally fitted.

4. Make the four 6mm holes along the edge of one long side. Fig 3.14 gives the dimensions used on the prototype but you must check the position of these holes (before drilling) to ensure that they will align with the cores of the coils.

5. When assembling the box, check that the holes coincide with the centre of the four coil cans. This will enable adjustments to be made when the unit has been boxed. When the performance of the signal generator seems satisfactory the box can be held in position by means of a few solder 'tacks' around the bottom edges. Do not solder continuously around the edge of the box as it will be difficult to remove at a later date in order to make modifications etc.

The prototype was fitted with a slow-motion drive to make it easier to set to a particular frequency. Details of this modification are given but it is appreciated that such drives can have rather high prices. The one used is known as 'epicyclic' and is indeed expensive.

The actual construction is shown in Fig 3.15 and needs little other detail. With some ingenuity any other slow-motion drive could be adapted to suit the generator. A card dial with four concentric circles drawn on it enables simple calibration to be carried out. It must be stressed that the instrument is a very low-cost and basic one, so laboratory standards must not be expected.

Audio-frequency oscillators

Coil and capacitor circuits are not usually used with these because the low frequencies require very large values. A different type of oscillator is normally used which does not make use of an oscillatory circuit. They are called 'relaxation oscillators'. Most produce a waveform that is far from a sine wave, being either triangular or

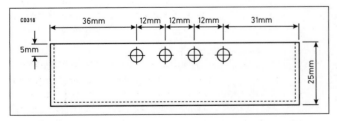

Fig 3.14. Positions of the holes in one long side of the screening box

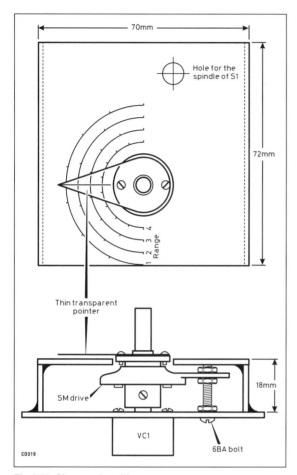

Fig 3.15. Slow-motion drive arrangement

The VFO, showing the holes which allow the coil cores to be adjusted

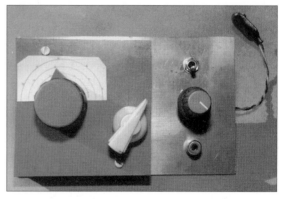

The completed VFO

square. When used as an audio signal they sound rather rough. This is because signals which are not sine waves contain voltages having frequencies which are a multiple of the original signal, for example twice, three times or four times etc). As you probably know, these are called 'harmonics'.

Two examples of audio oscillator are described: (a) a phase-shift oscillator which does produce a sine wave but with rather a low output and (b) a true relaxation oscillator which produces plenty of output but sounds a bit like a chain saw.

We will use an audio oscillator to provide 'sidetone' for a CW transmitter. This is necessary to allow the operator to hear his or her own signal. It is possible to get this effect by listening on the station receiver but this brings with it a number of complications. A sidetone oscillator is keyed at the same time as the transmitter and the resulting audio frequency fed into headphones or loudspeaker.

A phase-shift oscillator

Fig 3.16 shows the circuit of a phase-shift oscillator (TR1) followed by a simple impedance-matching transistor (TR2) which enables other circuits to be connected – in this case a crystal sounder. TR1 is an amplifier in which some of the output voltage is fed back into the input via

The slow-motion arrangement

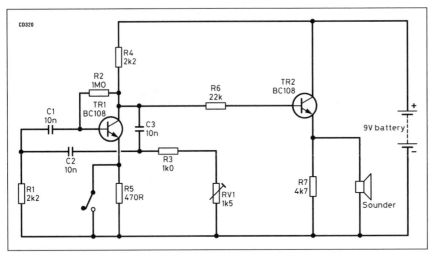

Fig 3.16. A phase-shift oscillator

Table 3.3. Components list for the phase-shift oscillator

RESISTORS

R1, 4	2k2
R2	1M0
R3	1k
R5	470R
R6	22k
R7	4k7

All resistors 0.5W carbon film.

CAPACITORS

C1, 2, 3 10n polyester

MISCELLANEOUS

TR1, 2   BC108 or equivalent

Piezo sounder (Maplin JH24B or equivalent)
Small piece of Veroboard – 10 tracks × 15 holes minimum
Battery clip for PP3

capacitors C3, C2 and C1. These capacitors, together with the associated resistors, cause a 180° phase shift at one frequency and the transistor amplifier oscillates at that frequency. The frequency at which this effect occurs is determined by the value of the components. RV1 is included to enable the frequency of the oscillation to be changed.

A components list for this project is given in Table 3.3.

In addition to gaining experience with a phase-shift oscillator, this project is included as an example of working with Veroboard. The construction is very simple; the layout shown in Fig 3.17 is easy to follow and should be sufficient for anyone wishing to build the oscillator. As a construction aid the tracks have been labelled from 'A' to 'J' and the columns of holes from '1' to '15'. Any hole can now be designated by giving the co-ordinates. For example, one end of R1 is taken through the hole J2 and the other end to hole A2. Note that the copper strips must be running horizontally across the board as it is drawn.

For anyone wishing to build the device using the above information, the co-ordinates for all components are given in Table 3.4.

Fig 3.17. Component layout on Veroboard

Table 3.4. Co-ordinates for phase-shift oscillator

R1: A2/J2
R2*: F9/G9
R3: B10/J10
R4: D11/G11
R5: A4/E4
R6*: E12/G12
R7: A15/F15
RV1: A5/C5/B9
C1: F3/J3
C2: J5/J7
C3: G8/J8
TR1: E5/G5/F6
TR2: E13/D14/F14
Key: A1/E1
Battery + red: D12
Battery – black: A12
Sounder: A13/F13
Break track: J6/F12/E8

* Mounted vertically.

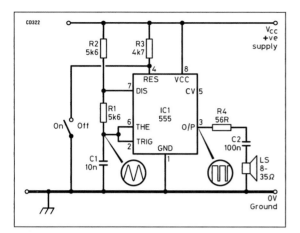

Fig 3.18. An AF oscillator using a 555 timer

The last item in Table 3.4 indicates that the copper track must be broken at these points to prevent a short-circuit between the other points on the track. This can be done by using a twist bit of about 3mm diameter held between the fingers – *not in a drill*.

The two components marked with an asterisk are mounted vertically, while the remaining ones lie flat on the board.

It must be stressed that the output is very small and will not be enough to operate a loudspeaker. The quality of the note is very good and could be classed as T9 in the RST code.

Table 3.5. Components list for the relaxation oscillator

RESISTORS
R1, 2   5k6
R3   4k7
R4   56R

CAPACITORS
C1   10n
C2   100n

MISCELLANEOUS
IC1   555 timer
LS   Any small loudspeaker, 8 to 35Ω

Switch, preferably a Morse key using top contact (normally closed)

All components can be mounted and interconnected using any of the methods described in Chapter 1.

A relaxation oscillator

This makes use of an integrated circuit type 555, called a 'timer'. The circuit is shown in Fig 3.18 and a components list is given in Table 3.5. It is very similar to the one used in the transmitter described in Chapter 5 and a full explanation of its function can be found in that chapter. Basically, the timer IC acts as a switch which opens and allows the capacitor C1 to charge via R1 and R2. After a time the switch closes and discharges C1 through R1. The action is continuous and a triangular waveform appears across the capacitor and a square wave occurs at the output of the IC, pin 3. A simple filter can be used to remove some of the harmonics from the output, making the waveform more acceptable.

Chapter 4

Amplifiers and filters

The maximum radio frequency power output of transmitters to be used by Novice licensees is 3W, and this enables the amplifiers to be of quite simple design. In addition the transistors used are relatively cheap, and this is certainly not true for devices providing high power as the cost goes up rather more rapidly than the power output!

RF amplifiers are often operated in Class B mode in the interests of efficiency. The transistor is unbiased and passes no current while there is no signal input. When a sine-wave signal is applied, the positive half of the cycle gets amplified and the negative half does not. Silicon transistors do not become conductive until the base is about 0.6V positive with respect to the emitter in the case of an NPN transistor and the same amount negative in the case of a PNP device. This means that when an AC voltage is applied between base and emitter the negative half-cycle and some part of the positive half-cycle will not cause any collector current to flow.

Fig 4.1 shows a simple Class B amplifier and Fig 4.2 some graphs indicating the relationship between the signal applied to the input and the resulting output. The alteration in the shape of the output signal is called 'harmonic distortion'. A tuned circuit in the output circuit of

the transistor will respond to the frequency to which it is tuned and, if this is the fundamental, the waveform will be reconstructed, leaving only a small amount of harmonic distortion. If the circuit is tuned to the second harmonic of the input it will respond to the harmonic and will 'contain' a signal having a frequency of twice that of the input. This effect is made use of in the FM transmitter described in Chapter 8 and is known as 'frequency doubling'.

However, when an amplitude-modulated signal is applied to an amplifier operated in Class B mode, the low-amplitude signals corresponding to low-level AF modulation will not cause the transistor to conduct at all and that part of the signal will be lost. Fig 4.3 illustrates this effect. The reconstruction mentioned above cannot take place as neither the positive nor negative half of the input will cause any output from the transistor. If a signal distorted in this way was received by a normal receiver the output would be badly distorted as only the louder passages of the audio signal would cause any output. To avoid this any amplifier used with amplitude-modulated

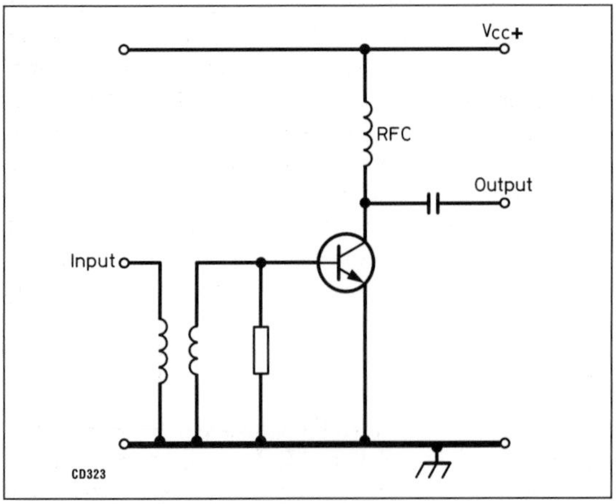

Fig 4.1. A simple Class B amplifier

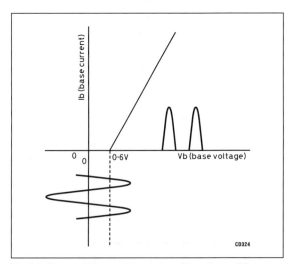

Fig 4.2. Some of the waveforms in a Class B amplifier

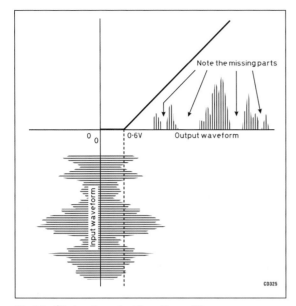

Fig 4.3. AM signals and a Class B amplifier

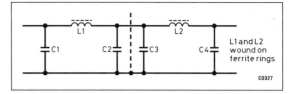

Fig 4.5. A practical form of low-pass filter

$$X_L = 2\pi f L$$

A capacitor behaves in the opposite manner – the capacitive reactance (opposition to a flow of alternating current) gets less as the frequency of the current increases. If you are wondering how current can flow 'through' a capacitor which contains an insulator it must be remembered that the voltage is continually rising or falling and the capacitor will be either charging or discharging. It is this current which appears to flow through the capacitor. Again, for the mathematically minded:

$$X_C = \frac{1}{2\pi f C}$$

Now refer to Fig 4.5. This shows a practical simple low-pass filter (LPF). If the values are correctly chosen, the reactance of C1 to the fundamental of the input will be moderately high and the reactance of the coil will be low. Similarly C2 will offer a moderately high reactance. The fundamental of the input will pass through the circuit with only little attenuation. At the frequency of the second harmonic the reactance of the two capacitors will be halved and the reactance of the coil will be doubled; the attenuation of the unwanted signal (the 'second harmonic') will be considerable. In practice it is normal to use two or three similar circuits following one another, C3, C4 and L2 in Fig 4.5 being the second LPF (low-pass filter).

With two circuits the effect is multiplied. For example, if one circuit reduces the second harmonic by a factor of four, then two circuits will reduce it by a factor of 16 and three circuits by a factor of 64. Higher harmonics cause the capacitive reactances to be even lower and the inductive reactance proportionately higher so that the attenuation of the higher harmonics is much greater. Remember that the second harmonic is likely to be much smaller than the fundamental at the input of the filter so that a further reduction of $1/16$ or even $1/64$ becomes very significant.

signals must be 'linear'. In other words, at least all of one half-cycle of the input must be treated without distortion. The other half-cycle is not important because of the reconstruction effect of tuned circuits already mentioned. When a transistor is biased so that it is conductive before any signal is applied, it is said to be operating in either 'Class AB' or in 'Class A'. In the latter mode the transistor is conductive at all times but the efficiency is low and the mode would not normally be used in battery-driven equipment.

As harmonics have frequencies which are a multiple of the original signal (the 'fundamental'), a circuit which will pass the fundamental but will stop any signal with a frequency of twice the fundamental frequency (or higher) will remove the harmonics and pass a sine wave to the output, in our case the antenna. A filter which will do this is called a 'low-pass filter'. It passes the low frequencies but not the higher ones. Fig 4.4 shows a simple low-pass filter.

The 'inductive reactance' of a coil is the name given to the opposition offered by some circuits, especially coils, to a flow of alternating current. The opposition gets larger as the frequency gets higher. For the mathematicians:

Matching

An amplifier must match the resistance of the load connected to it, if maximum efficiency is to be obtained. Consider a person riding a bicycle – on level ground it is fairly easy to keep the bike moving but when a hill is

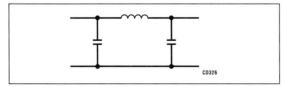

Fig 4.4. A very simple low-pass filter

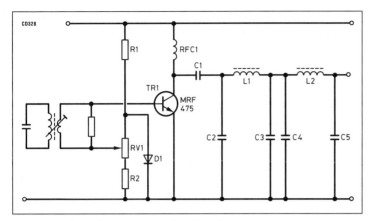

Fig 4.6. An RF power output stage for all modes

attempted it gets harder to keep going – the load has in-creased. The rider will probably change to a lower gear so that he or she must pedal faster to keep moving for-ward. As the hill gets steeper so the gear is reduced; the gear mechanism is matching the rider to the load. An amplifier also needs to be matched to its load.

There are a number of ways of doing this but at the powers used by Novices it is fortunate that almost no matching is needed. At this stage we will say that the output impedance of the amplifier is determined by the power output and the supply voltage. With a supply of 12V and a power of 1.5W, the output impedance will be just about 50Ω, which is very often the impedance of our antenna so the two things will match. Of course this as-sumes that the impedance of the antenna is 50Ω and not all of them will have this impedance. To get over the problem we can make use of an antenna tuning unit (ATU). Many antennas and some ATUs are described in the RSGB book *Practical Antennas for Novices* by John Heys, G3BDQ.

The circuit in Fig 4.6 shows an amplifier operating in Class AB mode (linear) which will give an output of about 1 to 1.5W when operated from 12V. The transistor is biased so that it is just conductive with no input signal. This bias is provided by R1, R2, RV1 and D1. It is im-portant that the bias does not change when there is a vari-ation in supply voltage. D1 provides this facility. The supply causes enough current to flow through D1 to pro-duce 'saturation' – in other words the voltage across the diode will not change when there is a change in supply voltage. The voltage required between base and emitter of the transistor is lower than that across D1, and RV1 allows the value to be adjusted. R2 is used to limit the range of variation given by RV1. In practice RV1 would be adjusted while the collector current of TR1 is monitored. The method is described in Chapter 7.

The amplifier can be made to operate on a number of

different frequencies simply by changing the values of the components which make up the low-pass filter.

If the power of the transistor is much higher (or lower) than 1 to 1.5W the output impedance will be lower (or higher) than 50Ω and some form of matching must be used between the output transis-tor and the antenna. There are many forms of matching circuit but only two will be described here. At low frequen-cies and/or low power a simple trans-former which can operate at the working frequency can be used. The circuit in Fig 4.7 shows how this is done but it must be remembered that the practical transformer may be quite different to those you have seen before. The construction of a typical RF transformer which can operate up to about 30MHz is shown in Fig 4.8. You will notice that the windings are not tuned and the transformer may be able to work successfully at all frequencies from Top Band (1.8 to 2.0MHz) through the amateur HF bands to 30MHz. Because of this they are often called 'wide-band transformers'.

In order that the transformer can cover such a wide band a number of conditions must be met. The number of turns must be kept small and this usually means that the smaller winding has only one turn. The inductance must be kept high and with a few turns there must be plenty of iron. The resistance of the windings must be low as considerable current may be carried. The 'leak-age inductance' must be very low. This means that there should be no loss of energy during the transfer from one winding to the other. To achieve this the windings must be very tightly coupled. There are a number of ways in which these criteria can be met, but the method shown in the diagram is very suitable for home construction.

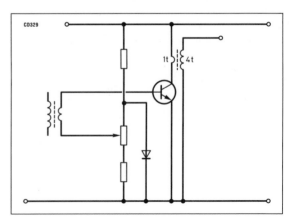

Fig 4.7. Matching by means of a transformer

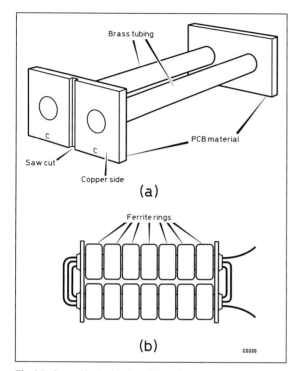

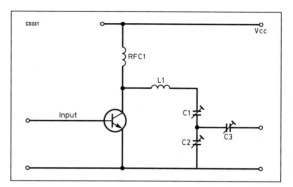

Fig 4.9. Matching for a VHF power amplifier

Fig 4.8. A practical wide-band transformer

Fig 4.8(a) shows two pieces of brass rod joined together by means of two pieces of copper laminate. One piece has a shallow saw cut across the centre while the other has the copper unbroken. In the finished article the four ends of the brass tubes are soldered to the copper laminate, producing a single-turn coil. Before one end is soldered, a number of ferrite rings are threaded on to the tubes as shown in Fig 4.8(b). The other winding is threaded through the tubes until the required number of turns is put on. The finished transformer is connected to the rest of the circuit by soldering the ends marked 'C' in Fig 4.8(a) to the correct points on the PCB. If the one-turn winding needs to be centre tapped the other end plate is also soldered to the PCB.

If the secondary of the transformer has four times as many turns as the primary it is referred to as a 'step-up transformer'. The impedance will be changed by a ratio of 1 to 16. A transistor operating from a supply rail of

13V and at an output power of about 75W will have an output impedance of about 4Ω, so that the above transformer would increase the output impedance from 4 to 48Ω which is the approximate value required by our antennas.

This method cannot be used on higher frequencies because the efficiency of the transformer decreases rapidly as the frequency gets higher. It is normal to use a combination of series- and parallel-tuned circuits to produce the impedance change.

Fig 4.9 shows a simple form of matching, making use of a series-tuned circuit. At resonance a series-tuned circuit has a very low impedance and, by choosing the correct values for the inductance L and the capacitance C, it is possible to make the circuit present the required low impedance to the output of the transistor. In the diagram the series circuit is formed by the combination of L1 with C1 and C2 in series. The RF choke (RFC) decouples the collector of the transistor from the supply. Although the total impedance of the circuit is low, the reactances of L and C are equal and high. For this reason C is split into two parts so that the required value of 50Ω can be obtained, with C3 usually included in practice to make the output resistive. The above explanation has been rather simplified – the full explanation requires considerable mathematics.

Unlike the transformer described in Fig 4.8, the circuit just described operates at the frequency to which it is tuned so that it can only be used with narrow-band amplifiers, but it has the great advantage that it helps to reduce harmonics from the transmitter output.

Chapter 5

An 80m CW transmitter

This chapter is based on an article by Steven Price, G4BWE, which appeared in the December 1991 issue of *Radio Communication*.

The Novice CW transmitter is intended to complement the RC14 beginner's HF receiver [1] and its matching 3.5MHz converter [2], both of which are available in kit form from Cirkit Distribution Ltd. However, the transmitter has been designed in such a way that it will easily interface with any receiver that covers 3.5MHz and can also resolve CW signals – in practice this means either a simple direct conversion receiver or a superhet with a product detector or BFO (the appropriate control may be marked 'SSB').

The 3.5MHz CW Novice segment is 20kHz (kilohertz) wide and extends upwards from 3.565MHz. In order to ensure a high level of frequency stability and also to prevent the possibility of the Novice transmitter accidentally being operated on a frequency outside the allotted segment, crystal control is employed. This involves the use of a separate quartz crystal (sometimes abbreviated 'xtal') for each frequency to be used. Up to four frequencies may be chosen and the appropriate crystal is then selected using a rotary switch mounted on the transmitter's front panel.

The four recommended frequencies are: XTAL1 – 3.567MHz; XTAL2 – 3.572MHz; XTAL3 – 3.577MHz; XTAL4 – 3.582MHz.

A complete kit of parts, which includes the high-quality PCB, all components, all connectors, hardware, solder, wire, and punched and painted custom-built case, is available from Cirkit Distribution Limited, Park Lane, Broxbourne, Hertfordshire, EN10 7NQ. Also supplied with the kit are two crystals – XTAL1 and XTAL2.

For the benefit of the more experienced constructors who may wish to build this project from scratch, rather than buy a kit, full constructional details are included.

Using CW

CW (continuous wave) transmisson is simplicity itself! All we need to do is build a generator of radio frequency (RF) energy – an oscillator – and arrange for it to be turned on and off using a morse key. Each time the key is depressed the generator emits a continuous stream of oscillations at the chosen frequency (the 'carrier wave'). The distant receiver then turns these oscillations into an audible tone so that the dots and dashes of morse code are rendered as bursts of sound in much the same way as they would be if we were using a morse code practice oscillator.

For practical use we may wish to increase the oscillator's power by feeding its output into an amplifier. A transmitting antenna is also necessary and it will obviously be convenient to use the same antenna for receive. This means that a switch of some kind must be incorporated so that the antenna can be connected to the transmitter when sending, and to the receiver when listening.

It is also a good idea to provide a means of monitoring the morse while it is being sent. One way of doing this is to use the station receiver. However, the results are likely to be unsatisfactory – mainly because the receiver will be grossly overloaded by a transmitter operating so close to it. The problem can be solved by building into the transmitter a tone generator controlled by the key – just like a practice oscillator. This technique is known as 'sidetone', and by adding further switching we can arrange for the tone to be fed to the receiver headphones during transmit.

Finally, the antenna and sidetone switching can be made automatic and activated by the morse key. The Novice transmitter offers all these features by incorporating logic control and a transmit/receive changeover relay. The design is therefore slightly more complex then absolutely necessary, but it is assumed that the Novice will wish to concentrate on the morse itself, rather than have to worry about switch settings!

How it works

Fig 5.1 shows a block diagram of the Novice transmitter and the full circuit appears in Fig 5.2. Transistor TR3 forms the heart of the crystal-controlled oscillator and S1 selects the appropriate quartz crystal (XTAL1 to XTAL4). TR2, the keying transistor, simply switches the

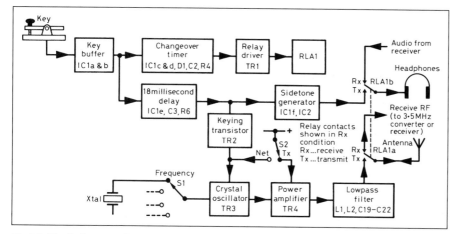

Fig 5.1. Block diagram of the Novice transmitter

oscillator on and off under the control of IC1 (more about IC1 later).

The main winding of T1 and C14 form a tuned circuit which is resonated at 3.5MHz. When TR3 is oscillating, its output is fed via the coupling winding of T1 to the base of the RF power transistor, TR4. R23 is a damping resistor which prevents excessive voltage appearing at the base of TR4 and also helps ensure that the power amplifier remains stable – we do not want TR4 to start oscillating as well!

Following amplification by TR4 the transmitter output is fed through a low-pass filter consisting of L1, L2 and C19 to C22.

The low-pass filter attenuates all frequencies above 3.5MHz. It is necessary to do this because the output from TR4 contains not just the 3.5MHz signal that we wish to transmit (known as the 'fundamental') but also the harmonics, or multiples, of this frequency. Omitting the low-pass filter would therefore cause the transmitter to radiate additional signals at 7MHz, 10.5MHz, 14MHz and so on; a situation we must clearly strive to avoid!

RFC1, a radio frequency choke, feeds power from the DC supply to TR4 but prevents RF currents travelling back in the opposite direction. The decoupling capacitors C23 to C25 help prevent instability by absorbing any RF energy that RFC1 fails to suppress.

IC1 contains six inverting gates labelled 'a' to 'f'. Each gate is a simple circuit made up of a few MOS transistors (MOS stands for 'metal oxide semiconductor' – but don't worry if you have not come across this expression before). An inverter is a logic device which provides an output voltage that is the opposite of its input. However, logic circuits can only operate by differentiating between two distinct levels – logic 0 and logic 1 (in a computer system these levels are used to represent the noughts and ones of binary numbers). Conveniently, logic 0 is defined

as zero volts and logic 1 is equal to the supply voltage – say 12V. So, if we connect the input of an inverter to the 12V supply rail, its output will immediately drop to 0V. Looking at the circuit symbol, the output is at the point of the triangle (the small circle here indicates that the gate is an inverting type).

Gates 'a' and 'b' of IC1 have their inputs connected ('tied' in logic circuit terms) to the supply rail via R2 and R9. Pins 2 and 4 will therefore be at 0V. As capacitor C2 is fully charged, pin 5 is also at 0V which means that pins 6 and 9 are at 12V. Pin 8, of course, gives an output of 0V and this ensures that TR1, the relay driver transistor, is turned off.

Now, if the morse key is depressed, pins 1 and 3 are grounded via R1 (the value of R1 is so small compared to R2 that the gates react as if they were connected directly to 0V). Pins 2 and 4 immediately go 'high' (another way of saying that the gate outputs rise to the supply voltage) and C2 discharges because both ends of this capacitor are now connected to 12V, albeit via R3 and D1. The states of IC1c and IC1d are also reversed and so TR1 switches on because pin 8 is now at 12V. This energises the coil of RLA1 – the transmit/receive changeover relay – and its contacts, RLA1a and RLA1b, move into the transmit position (NB in Figs 5.1 and 5.2 the relay contacts are shown in the receive position).

The purpose of RLA1a is to connect the antenna to the output of the low-pass filter on transmit, but allow the receiver to be connected to the antenna when listening. This is achieved by phono socket SK2 using a patch lead which enables the antenna socket of the receiver (or the 3.5MHz converter) to be coupled to SK2.

When the morse key is released, pins 1 and 3 of IC1 go high (+12V) and pins 2 and 4 return to 0V. However, as C2 has been discharged, the input of IC1c (pin 5) initially remains high and so TR1 stays switched on. C2 now begins slowly to charge through R4 (the outputs of gates 'a' and 'b' play no part at this point because they are isolated by D1 which is reversed biased and therefore cannot conduct). After about two seconds, C2 is charged sufficiently to take the input of IC1c low (ie close to 0V) and so TR1 finally switches off and the relay contacts return to the receive position. Of course, if the morse key is pressed again at any time before the input of IC1c goes

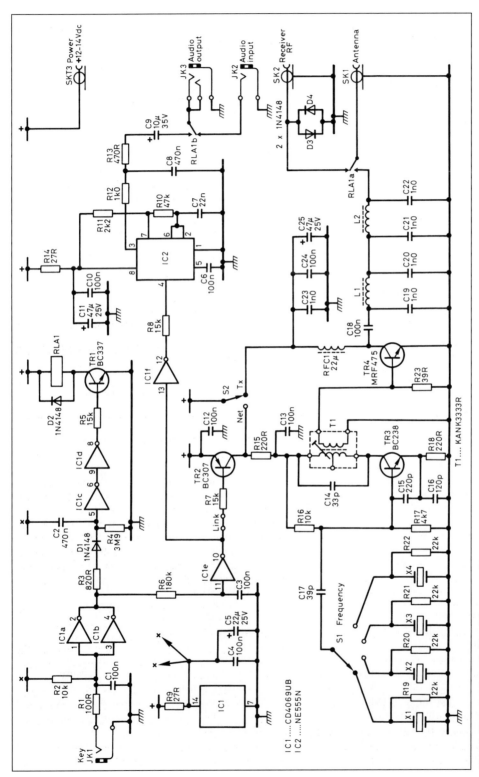

Fig 5.2. The complete circuit of the transmitter

Table 5.1. Components list

RESISTORS		INDUCTORS		MISCELLANEOUS	
R1	100R	L1, 2	See text	RLA1	Iskra TRK2233 (12V, 270Ω coil)
R2, 16	10k	RFC1	22µH Toko 8RBSH	S1	3-pole, 4-way rotary type CK1026
R3	820R		(Part No 262LYF-0084K)	S2	SPDT miniature toggle
R4	3M9	T1	Toko 10K type KANK3333R	SK1	SO239 (single-hole fixing type)
R5, 7, 8	15k			SK2	Phono (single-hole fixing type)
R6	180k	**SEMICONDUCTORS**		SK3	2.5mm DC power socket
R9, 14	27R	D1–4	1N4148	JK1, 2	6.3mm mono jack socket
R10	47k	TR1	BC337	JK3	6.3mm stereo jack socket
R11	2k2	TR2	BC307		
R12	1k	TR3	BC238	8-pin DIL IC socket	
R13	470R	TR4	MRF475	14-pin DIL IC socket	
R15, 18	220R	IC1	CD4069UB	2.5mm coaxial DC power plug	
R17	4k7	IC2	NE555N	PL259 plug with solderless reducer for RG58U cable	
R19–22	22k			Phono plugs (two required), all metal	
R23	39R			Two 6.3mm mono jack plugs	

All resistors are 0.25W, 5% carbon film.

CAPACITORS

C1, 4, 6, 10,	
12, 13, 24	100n disc ceramic
C2, 8	470n Siemens-style polyester, 10mm lead spacing
C3, 18	100n Siemens style polyester, 10mm lead spacing
C5	22µ 25V radial electrolytic
C7	22µ Siemens-style polyester, 10mm lead spacing
C9	10µ 35V radial electrolytic
C11, 25	47µ 25V radial electrolytic
C14	33p sub-miniature ceramic plate
C15	220p sub-miniature ceramic plate
C16	120p sub-miniature ceramic plate
C17	39p sub-miniature ceramic plate
C19–22	1n polystyrene
C23	1n disc ceramic

6.3mm stereo jack plug
1.2m of RG174A/U miniature coaxial cable
Multicore solder
PVC-covered, stranded cable for flying leads and PCB link
1m of 24swg enamelled copper wire
PCB and case with lid (see text)
Heatsink for TR4 (type TV-5)
Small quantity of heat transfer compound
Trimmer tool for T1 (Cirkit part No 35-00002)
Four 6BA nuts, bolts (15mm overall length) and 6.3mm spacers to mount PCB
4BA nut and bolt (short) plus shake-proof washer to fix heatsink
Two self-tapping screws (small) to fix lid
Four stick-on feet
Two T68-2 powdered iron toroids (for L1, 2)
6.3mm push-on knob plus cap with index line (for S1)
XTAL1–4 – see text

low, the process is halted and C2 must begin charging all over again.

The net result of all this is that once we have started to send morse, RLA1 stays in the transmit position until there is a pause of approximately two seconds. This prevents RLA1 attempting to follow every depression of the key and ensures that the receiver remains disconnected from the antenna during the whole period of transmission.

The morse itself is routed via R6 and IC1e to the keying transistor TR2. R6 and C3 delay the dots and dashes by a period of 18 milliseconds (one millisecond equals one thousandth of a second). This small delay is introduced so as to ensure that RLA1 has time to connect the output of the power amplifier (TR4) to the antenna before the oscillator (TR3) has been activated by TR2.

The output of IC1e is inverted by IC1f in order to key the sidetone generator built around the NE555 oscillator/timer chip, IC2. The NE555 produces an audio tone in similar fashion to a morse practice oscillator – indeed, you may already have seen designs for practice oscillators which utilise this popular IC. The frequency (pitch) of the tone is determined by R10, R11 and C7 and is set at approximately 700Hz. IC2's output is taken from pin

3 and filtered to make it sound more pleasant by R12 and C8. R13 attenuates the tone so that it is not too loud in the headphones.

Instead of plugging the headphones into the receiver as normal, a jack socket (JK3) is provided for the 'phones on the front panel of the transmitter. A patch lead couples the receiver's headphone socket to JK2 and this enables us to listen to the receiver when RLA1b is in the receive position. However, as soon as the key is depressed at the beginning of a transmission, RLA1b connects the headphones to the sidetone generator so that we can hear the morse being sent.

Finally, S2 (the 'net switch') enables us to turn on the crystal oscillator without having to depress the key. This means that RLA1 will stay in the receive position and we can listen to the oscillator using the receiver as a monitor. This enables us to tune the receiver to our transmit frequency (very important). Note that when 'netting' (the name given to the process whereby the receiver and transmitter are tuned to the same frequency), TR4 is disconnected from the power supply as there is no need for the oscillator signal to be amplified.

The completed transmitter will provide an output power of just over 1W if operated from a 12V power

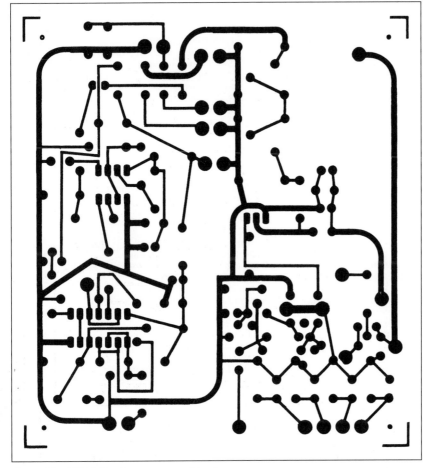

Fig 5.3. The PCB foil pattern – copper side shown

You will also need a trimming tool for T1 (Note that this is supplied with the kit).

The first job for those who have not purchased the kit will be the preparation of the printed circuit board. Fig 5.3 shows the foil pattern for this.

Now proceed as follows:

1. Wind L1 and L2 using the 24swg enamelled copper wire. Start by cutting the length supplied (1m) in half and then tightly wind 20 turns (avoid overlapping) onto one of the doughnut-shaped powdered iron toroids. Cut the tails of the winding to a length of approx 10mm and carefully scrape away the enamel (which serves as insulation) from the tails using wire cutters – this will make soldering easier later. Now prepare the other inductor but make sure that you wind it in the opposite direction.

2. Fig 5.4 shows the printed circuit board component layout. Start by mounting some of the larger components – T1, RLA1 and the two IC sockets. T1 is enclosed in a tin-plated screening can which has two earthing tags. Solder these and the five pins which protrude from the underside of T1. The IC sockets are coloured black (Note: do not insert IC1 and IC2 at this stage). RLA1 has a white rectangular casing with the manufacturer's name (Iskra) printed on the top.

3. The resistors are all mounted horizontally with their leads bent at right-angles.

4. Next mount the electrolytic capacitors (C5, 9, 11 and 25). These components are polarised and must be positioned the correct way round. The four polystyrene capacitors (C19 to C22) are tubular in shape and have translucent plastic bodies through which can be seen the metal foil that forms their plates. They will either be marked '1nJ' or '1000J' ('1000' meaning '1000pF' which is the same as 1nF). C19 to C22 are mounted horizontally.

supply (slightly more using 13.8V). This is comfortably within the 3W power limit specified by the Novice Licence regulations.

Construction

Now that the transmitter has been described and the block and circuit diagrams given, here's how to build it. Those who obtain the kit will only require a few basic tools in order to successfully complete this project:

- A soldering iron of between 15 and 25W rating (no higher unless thermostatically controlled), having a bit diameter no greater than 1.5mm.
- A small pair of wire cutters.
- A flat-bladed screwdriver; 4mm blade width is suitable.
- A junior hacksaw.

Details and advice on the above and on other tools is given in Appendix 1.

5. The polyester capacitors (C2, 3, 7, 8 and 18) are rectangular in shape and have metal end-plates to which their leads are spot welded – do not attempt to bend these leads as they can easily be broken off. The value and working voltage (the latter either 100 or 250) is marked but you may find that 100nF and 470nF are shown as 'm1' and 'm47' respectively.

6. The remaining ceramic capacitors are fairly easy to identify. They will probably be biscuit coloured, although C14 to C17 may also be spotted at the top with either orange, red or black paint. The 1nF and 100nF values are normally shown as '102' and '104' respectively. You may have to bend the leads of the smaller ceramics outwards slightly prior to mounting.

7. Diodes D1 to D4 are the smallest components. They must be mounted the correct way round, as shown in Fig 5.4. Transistors TR1 to TR3 have a flat face carrying their markings. Mount them with this face in the direction indicated by Fig 5.4.

8. RFC1 consists of a grey ferrite bobbin pre-wound with enamelled copper wire. The top surface of RFC1 will be marked with the type number '0084K'. The quartz crystals are sealed into tin-plated cans and have their frequencies either printed or engraved on one side.

9. The link which connects pins 10 and 13 of IC1 to R7 is now inserted. This is made by cutting a short length (85 to 90mm) of insulated cable and bareing each

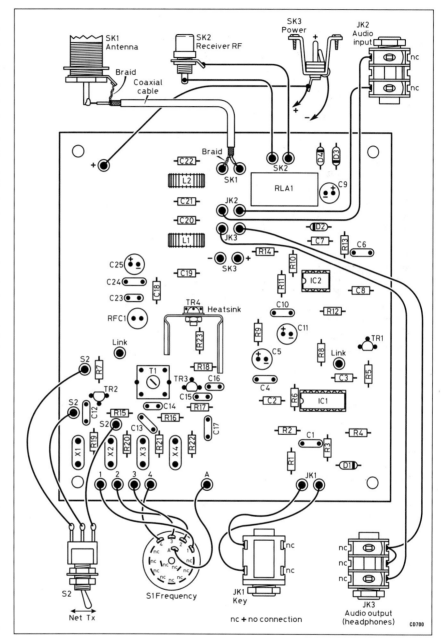

Fig 5.4. Component information and soldering

end with the wire cutters prior to soldering. Now mount L1 and L2 so that they are positioned as shown in Fig 5.4.

10. The final component to be mounted is TR4. However, it is necessary to bolt the heatsink to TR4 first. Fig 5.5(a) illustrates how this is done. Note that the fins on one side of the heatsink (which is made of

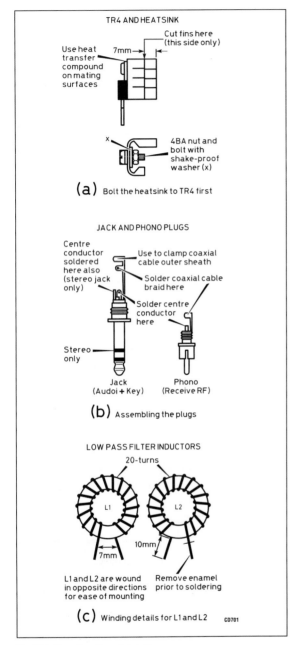

TR4 AND HEATSINK

Use heat transfer compound on mating surfaces

7mm

Cut fins here (this side only)

4BA nut and bolt with shake-proof washer (x)

(a) Bolt the heatsink to TR4 first

JACK AND PHONO PLUGS

Centre conductor soldered here also (stereo jack only)

Use to clamp coaxial cable outer sheath

Solder coaxial cable braid here

Solder centre conductor here

Stereo only

Jack (Audoi + Key)

Phono (Receive RF)

(b) Assembling the plugs

LOW PASS FILTER INDUCTORS

20-turns

L1   L2

10mm

7mm

L1 and L2 are wound in opposite directions for ease of mounting

Remove enamel prior to soldering

(c) Winding details for L1 and L2   CD701

Fig 5.5. Constructional detail

aluminium painted black) must be shortened by 7mm using a hacksaw – this prevents the heatsink, which will be 'live', touching the screening can of T1. Remember to apply some heat transfer compound to the rear surface of TR4's metal cooling tab before bolting it to the heatsink as shown. Once the heatsink has been attached, TR4 may be soldered in place.

11. The next job is to cut and solder the various flying leads. Fig 5.4 shows what is required, but you may also wish to take a look at the case in order to gauge the relative positions of the sockets and switches – this will give a better idea of how long each lead needs to be. Consider 'colour coding' the leads as appropriate – for example, use cable with red insulation for the positive connections to SK3. It is preferable to make the leads slightly long at this stage as their far ends can always be trimmed before being soldered to the respective switch or socket. Also, remember that where two leads go to the same socket, they are best twisted together and this tends to make them shorter (the flying leads have not been shown twisted in Fig 5.4 for clarity).

12. The flying lead for SK1 (antenna) is made from a length of miniature coaxial cable. Be careful when stripping the outer sheath from this as it is very easy to cut through the braid as well.

13. Final assembly involves soldering the far ends of the flying leads to their respective sockets and switches and then bolting the printed circuit board into the case using the four 6BA nuts and bolts – remember to use the spacing pillars here, otherwise the underside of the circuit board will short-circuit against the aluminium case.

Other points to bear in mind are as follows:

- JK1 is mounted with its solder tags pointing upwards whereas JK2 and JK3 have their tags pointing downwards. Note the link joining two of the tags on JK3. A number of tags are left unconnected (ie those marked 'nc' in Fig 5.4).
- Only five of the tags on S1 are used. Those marked 'B', 'C' and '5' to '12' are not connected (S1 is actually a three-pole switch but only one pole is required in this design). Prior to soldering S1, cut its control spindle to length (approximately 9mm is suitable for the push-on knob supplied) using the hacksaw.
- SK3 has three solder tags. The two positive leads both go to the tag which protrudes from the rear of SK3. The negative lead is soldered to the tag which rests against the metal U-frame of the socket. The tag which is sandwiched between two layers of insulating material is not used.
- It will not be possible to solder the centre connections of SK1 and SK2 until after these sockets have been bolted in place. However, it is a good idea to solder the earthing tags prior to doing this, otherwise the case will conduct heat away from the earth tags and prevent them reaching a high enough temperature during the soldering operation.

14. IC1 and IC2 may now be inserted. Look for the notch in the encapsulation of these components and mount

them in the direction indicated by Fig 5.4. It may be necessary to bend the IC leads inwards slightly to match the spacing between the two lines of holes in the IC sockets. Integrated circuits can be damaged by static electricity (this applies particularly to IC1) so avoid wearing clothes that are known to generate static, such as nylon.

15. Before the transmitter can be tested it will be necessary to make up a power lead using the plug provided with the kit, ensuring, of course, that the positive lead is the one connected to the centre pin of the plug! Two coaxial patch leads are also required – one for receive RF, which has a phono plug at each end, and one for receiver audio which has a mono jack plug at one end and a stereo jack plug at the other. To make these, cut the remaining miniature coaxial cable in half and solder the plugs using Fig 5.5(b) as a guide. If you do not plan to use the RC14 + 3.5MHz converter you may, of course, need to use different plugs at the receiver end.

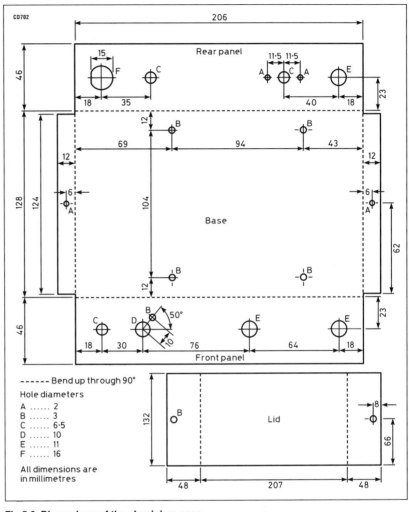

Fig 5.6. Dimensions of the aluminium case

For constructors who have not obtained the kit, Fig 5.6 shows the case dimensions. The material is 18swg aluminium.

Testing

Fig 5.7 shows the layout of the front and rear panels. S1 has four positions but remember that if you only have two crystals then settings three and four will be inactive.

The transmitter is designed to work with an antenna that presents a non-reactive load of approximately 50Ω at 3.5MHz. This means that we can employ a 50Ω resistor as a substitute for the antenna while tests are made. The advantage of using such a resistor (known as a

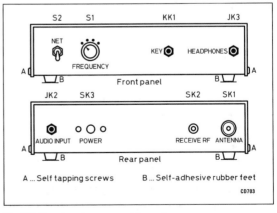

Fig 5.7. Front and rear panel layout

'dummy load') is that all the RF power generated by the transmitter will be converted into heat, rather than being radiated as a signal. Using a dummy load therefore avoids causing interference to other stations.

As the transmitter has an output of just over 1W, our dummy load must be capable of dissipating this much power without overheating. Unfortunately, standard carbon film resistors of the type used in the transmitter are rated at only 0.25W. Larger carbon resistors rated at 1 or 2W are available and one of these with a value of 47Ω could be used (*note:* avoid wirewound types – these are not suitable for use at radio frequencies). Alternatively, a 50Ω 1.25W resistor can be made by connecting five 10Ω 0.25W carbon film resistors in series, but make sure that the resistors are soldered close together.

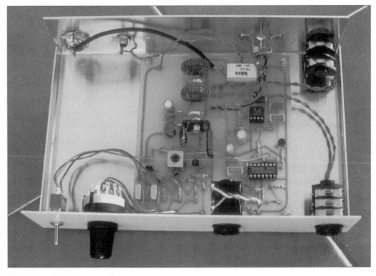

The completed transmitter

Fig 5.8 shows how the dummy load may be used in conjunction with a standard multimeter. The diode and capacitor (a disc ceramic type is suitable) convert the alternating RF voltage generated by the transmitter into DC so that the multimeter can give a sensible reading (more about this later). The diode and capacitor must be positioned close to the dummy load – you could mount all the components on a small piece of Veroboard. The dummy load must be coupled to the transmitter's antenna socket using coaxial cable. The length of the cable is unimportant and so it is possible to use the antenna feeder cable temporarily before this is attached to the dipole T-piece.

The dummy load has been described now because it is a good idea to couple this to the transmitter before first switching on the power supply and then leave it connected while all other tests are made.

Now plug one end of the phono patch lead into the transmitter's receive RF socket (SK2) and the other end into the 3.5MHz converter's antenna socket (the converter should, of course, be coupled to the RC14 for 3.5MHz

reception using its own patch lead). The stereo jack plug of the audio patch lead is plugged into the RC14 headphone socket and the mono jack plug inserted into the transmitter's audio input socket (JK2). The headphones are now plugged into the audio output socket (JK3) on the transmitter's front panel. The morse key must have a mono jack plug soldered to its lead (this is supplied with the kit) so that it can be plugged into the front panel key socket (JK1).

The transmitter, 3.5MHz converter and RC14 may now be connected to the power supply and the supply switched on. Using a multimeter with its negative test lead connected to ground (the case of the transmitter can be used for this), carefully check that 12V (assuming that this is the normal supply voltage) appears at the rear of the transmitter power socket (SK3). If all is well, set S2 to the net position, put the headphones on and listen for the receiver's background noise (remember that you are unlikely to hear any signals as we have a dummy load connected instead of the antenna).

Now press the key and check that the sidetone generator operates correctly. On releasing the key, the headphones should go dead for about two seconds and then the receiver background noise will return – this confirms that the changeover timer is functioning as intended. If there is no audio, take the headphones off and tap the key – you should be able to hear the changeover relay (RLA1) click once as you tap and then click again two seconds later. Minor faults can be detected using the multimeter – check, for instance, that the integrated circuits are both powered-up by measuring on their supply pins (pin 14 of IC1 and pin 8 of IC2). Also, measure the voltage on pins 1 and 3 of IC1 – there should be 12V

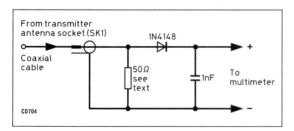

Fig 5.8. The dummy load and meter interface

when the key is up but hardly any voltage when the key is depressed.

Finally, make absolutely sure that D1 and D2 are mounted the right way round!

The multimeter is now connected to the dummy load and rectifier circuit (Fig 5.8). Switch S2 to TX (transmit) and check that S1 is set so as to select a crystal. Depress the key and keep it held down (it may be easier to adjust the key so that its contacts short out – this will leave you with both hands free). There may or may not be a voltage reading at this point. Now adjust the core of T1 using the plastic trimming tool provided (the core is like a grub screw but is made of rather brittle ferrite material – so be gentle with it!). At a certain point, probably with the core positioned fairly low down into T1, a reading will be obtained (or will simply increase). The reading will peak at a certain point and this is the required setting. About 10 to 12V DC can be expected and this reading may be used to calculate the power output of the transmitter using the following formula (V is the reading obtained in volts):

$$\frac{(V + 0.6)^2}{100} = \text{Power (W)}$$

As an example, let us assume that the reading is 9.4V.

9.4 + 0.6 = 10
10 squared (ie 10 multiplied by 10) = 100
100 divided by 100 = 1

So the output power is one watt.

For those who are curious, we must add 0.6 to the reading in order to compensate for the unavoidable voltage drop across the diode. The reason for using the figure 100 in the calculation is a little more complex – but don't feel that you need to know everything at this stage!

It should now be possible to key the transmitter as you would if sending morse – check that when the key is up the output voltage drops to zero. This confirms that the carrier is being interrupted by the key. Finally, reduce the receiver's volume again and set S2 to the NET position. The crystal oscillator will now operate continuously. Tune the receiver until you hear a loud tone and check that the frequency is close to that of the selected

crystal (if you are using a receiver with digital read-out it is possible to gauge this more accurately). The tone is rather loud and so it is a good idea to pull the headphones away from your ears while 'netting'.

Later, when using the transmitter on the air, always attempt to tune the receiver so that the net tone is of the same pitch as the note produced by the sidetone generator. Those using the RC14 CW filter [3] will find that this pitch corresponds with the peak of the filter's response.

If you are using a superhet receiver with a control marked 'LSB/USB', but no CW position, simply select 'USB'.

Modifications

Depending on personal taste and the characteristics of your headphones etc, you may wish to consider the following modifications:

1. The sidetone volume can be lowered by increasing the value of R13. Try 1kΩ for a moderate reduction or perhaps 2.2kΩ for greater attenuation.
2. More-experienced operators may prefer a shorter changeover delay. This can be achieved by reducing the value of R4. For instance, 2.2MΩ will give a delay of approximately one second.
3. It has been noticed when using the transmitter in conjunction with the 3.5MHz converter that a temporary power rail short may occur when removing the converter's patch lead jack from its bypass socket (this can therefore only happen if you have been listening on 14MHz). The problem is related to D3 which provides a current path to ground. Simply breaking the connection to the centre of SK2 (receive RF) and inserting a 10nF disc ceramic in series with the flying lead will cure this.

References

[1] 'The RC14 Beginners Receiver', *Radio Communication* June 1987, pp397–399.
[2] 'A 3.5MHz Converter for the RC14', *Radio Communication* April 1989, pp39–42.
[3] 'CW Filter for the RC14', *Radio Communication* July 1989, pp42–44.

Chapter 6

Modulation and modulators

Transmitters like the one described in Chapter 5 only radiate a radio frequency signal. The data (information) is carried by the RF by means of switching the transmitter on and off, normally by the operator and the morse key. If it becomes necessary to transmit speech then some way of making the RF 'carry' the audio frequencies must be found. There are a number of ways in which this can be done but we will consider only two of them – amplitude modulation and frequency modulation.

Amplitude modulation

This is a system in which the audio frequencies are mixed with the radio frequency so that the amplitude (power) of the RF increases and decreases in time with the AF. Fig 6.1 shows a graph which will help to make the idea clearer.

The function can be described in another way which at first appears to be quite different. When signals of different frequencies are mixed together new frequencies are produced which are equal to the sum and the difference of the two frequencies. For example if a radio frequency of 3.700MHz is to be used as a carrier and an audio frequency of 1kHz (0.001MHz) is mixed with it then two new frequencies will be produced; these will have values of 3.701MHz and 3.699MHz. They are

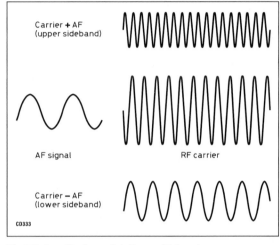

Fig 6.2. Amplitude modulation – sidebands

known as the 'upper and lower sidebands'. Fig 6.2 illustrates this graphically.

For those who are mathematically inclined it will be apparent that for every different audio frequency there will be two unique sidebands – one higher than the carrier by the value of the audio frequency and the other lower than the carrier by the same amount.

At the receiver only one sideband is needed (for each audio frequency) and the carrier is only necessary as a reference. Therefore it is possible for the transmitter to radiate only one set of sidebands – the carrier can be put in at the receiver. The sidebands mix with the re-inserted carrier and again produce sum and difference frequencies.

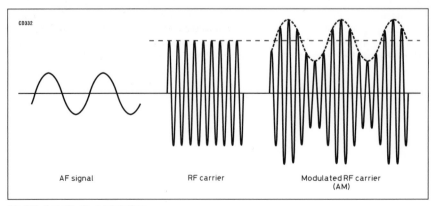

Fig 6.1. Amplitude modulation

Using the figures used previously, if a sideband having a frequency of 3.699MHz mixes with the carrier (put in by the receiver) of 3.700MHz, two new frequencies will be generated. These are 7.399MHz (the sum) and 0.001MHz or 1kHz (the difference). The higher frequency will be eliminated by the audio amplifier circuits but the lower one, which is equal to the original modulating frequency, will pass through to the output.

This type of modulation is known as 'single sideband, suppressed carrier' or 'SSB' for short. It is still amplitude modulation.

Radio amateur AM transmitters which operate in the lower HF bands (7.1MHz or less) usually make use of the lower sidebands. Those above that frequency use the upper sideband. These terms are often abbreviated to 'LSB' and 'USB'.

Why go to all the trouble – what is wrong with the original idea of amplitude modulation? There are two major advantages of SSB. The bandwidth required by the transmission is about half that needed by a full AM transmission. If a transmitter is able to deal with all audio frequencies up to 3kHz the full AM system will have to be able to radiate all frequencies from 3kHz below the carrier up to 3kHz above it – a bandwidth of 6kHz. With SSB the bandwidth will be reduced to 3kHz because one set of sidebands will be absent. Even more important, the transmitter does not have to radiate the carrier and one set of sidebands and therefore the power required is much less. Conversely, if the maximum output of a transmitter is limited to 3W, all of that power can be contained in the one set of sidebands in an SSB transmitter but will have to be shared between the carrier and two sets of sidebands in the full AM transmitter.

There must be some disadvantage! Both the transmitter and receiver are considerably more complex and the receiver is not so easy to tune. The operator must adjust the frequency of the carrier which is re-inserted at the receiver and must do this to make the voice of the operator of the remote transmitter sound right, very often without knowing what it sounds like anyway!

Frequency modulation

In this mode the audio frequencies cause the frequency of the carrier to vary above and below its normal value. A high audio frequency will make the frequency of the carrier change rapidly, while a low AF will cause it to

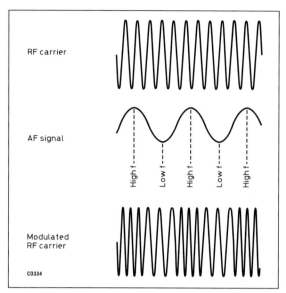

Fig 6.3. Frequency modulation

change more slowly. An AF with a big amplitude (loud) will make the carrier frequency change a lot while one with a low amplitude (quiet) will cause it to change only a little. The amplitude of the carrier does not change. As most static interference caused by sparking at switch contacts and electric motors etc comes in the form of amplitude modulation, an FM receiver will not be affected by this type of interference as much as an AM receiver would be.

The bandwidth required by an FM transmission depends on the limits set on the variation of the frequency of the carrier above and below the nominal carrier frequency. In order to maintain reasonable speech quality a 'deviation' (the name given to the change in frequency) of plus and minus 3kHz is necessary. The bandwidth of such a transmission cannot be less than about 12kHz and is often as high as 25kHz. Although not so easy to visualise, sidebands are generated and must not be attenuated too much as the audio quality depends on them.

There is no need to understand the complexities of this system of modulation at this stage. The type of circuit which carries out the modulation in the above two systems will be described in Chapters 7 and 8 when the transmitters are described.

Chapter 7

A double-sideband transmitter for Top Band

This is probably the most complicated of the HF designs described in this book and should not be attempted until some of the other projects have been satisfactorily completed. It was originally intended that the transmitter be dual mode, offering both CW and amplitude modulation so that it would be suitable for use as the hidden transmitter in direction-finding exercises. (The CW mode is used for the normal DF signal and the AM for giving instructions to the competitors who may not be able to read morse code.) Rather than offering normal AM (double sideband together with full carrier) it has been decided that double-sideband, suppressed-carrier (DSB) would be simpler, more economical in battery consumption and of greater interest as it gives an introduction to the more commonly used single-sideband (SSB) mode.

It may be that some constructors do not wish to use the transmitter for CW operation and therefore the construction has been arranged so that the DSB part is completed before work on the CW part is commenced.

There are a number of similarities with the 80m CW transmitter described in Chapter 5 and therefore details of some of the construction will not be repeated. Refer to Chapter 5 if there appear to be some omissions.

Circuit

The circuit shown in Fig 7.1 contains many points of similarity to that of the 80m transmitter and only the differences will be described in detail. TR1 is the carrier generator and is almost identical to the crystal oscillators already used in several other projects. The four crystals can be of any frequency within the Novice Top Band allocation. Do not use a crystal frequency higher than 1.99MHz to avoid sideband breakthrough above 2.0MHz. If the transmitter is to be used unattended in the course of direction-finding exercises one of the crystals should be 1.86MHz – the frequency allocated for this purpose.

TR2 is a buffer amplifier which drives the balanced modulator. This consists of T1 and the two diodes, D1 and D2. The transformer has a secondary which is centre tapped so that equal voltages occur across each half. The

diodes are biased by a combination of the voltage developed across R11 and that across RV1. This preset control is adjusted so that with no audio frequency signal present the two diodes conduct equally and the resultant signal across R17 is zero. In other words the carrier has been cancelled out because the RF signals are taken from opposite ends of the secondary of T1.

Audio voltages from the microphone are amplified by the operational amplifier IC1. The gain of this amplifier is adjustable by changing the value of the feedback resistor RV2. Audio frequencies lower than 300Hz are attenuated by the coupling capacitors C37, C12 and C10 and those above 3kHz are attenuated by the feedback capacitor C39 (which increases the negative feedback to signals above 3kHz) and by C* and C* across the input and output of TR5 if required. TR5 is a buffer amplifier which feeds the audio signals to the centre tap on the secondary of T1. The conductivity of the two diodes will be changed by these voltages as the bias is moved up and down in time with the audio frequency. Radio frequency signals will appear across R17 which will be the upper and lower sidebands. These are applied to the base of TR4, the driver RF amplifier. T2 primary in the collector circuit is tuned to the carrier frequency and the voltage developed across the secondary is used to drive the power output stage. This is similar to the output stage used in the 80m transmitter of Chapter 5 but as it is to be used for speech as well as CW it must be linear.

As already explained in Chapter 4, at least one half-cycle must be amplified with minimum distortion. To achieve this, the transistor is biased so that it is conductive for all of the positive half-cycle and a very small part of the negative half-cycle. The simple amplifier in the 80m transmitter does not conduct until the base of the transistor reaches about 0.7V. Hence, if this type of amplifier was used for SSB or DSB, any weak signals of less than 0.7V at the base of the transistor would not be amplified at all, causing very severe distortion of the transmitted signal. The bias for TR4 is provided by R22, RV3 and D5. The method of setting the bias level will be described later.

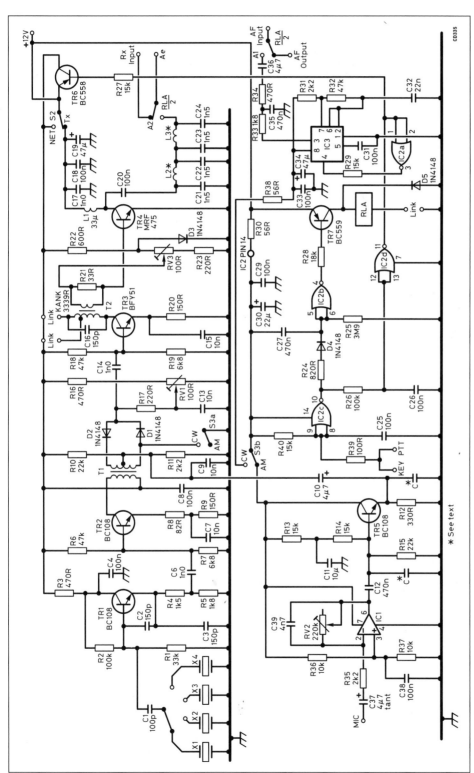

Fig 7.1. Circuit diagram of the CW/DSB transmitter

The CW function of the transmitter is provided in an unusual fashion. When S3 is put to the CW position the balanced mixer becomes totally unbalanced, so that when TR1, 2 and 3 are switched on by the action of the morse key the carrier signal is applied to the output stage.

The switching logic is very similar to the circuit used in the 80m transmitter but in this case it is provided by four NOR gates contained in IC2. Each gate is used as a simple inverter, the two inputs being connected together in each case. The main difference is the use of PNP transistors for TR6 and TR7 so that these transistors become fully conductive ('saturated') when the base is driven towards zero volts. When pin 11 of IC2d goes low (zero volts), TR6 switches on and connects the positive supply to TR1, TR2 and TR3, causing the transmitter to switch on. At the same time pin 4 of IC2b goes low, causing TR7 to conduct which in turn energises the antenna relay. By referring to Chapter 5 you should be able to work out how the remainder of the control circuit reacts when the key or the PTT (press-to-talk) switch is operated.

The function of D4 was explained fully in Chapter 5 but D5 may appear to be unnecessary as it appears to be connected in such a way that it can never conduct. It must be remembered that when TR7 becomes conductive the relay coil passes a fairly large current and considerable energy is stored in the magnetic field which holds the relay closed. When TR7 ceases to conduct the magnetic field around the relay coil collapses and generates a high voltage which will be positive at the earthy end of the relay coil. The voltage may have a value of several hundred volts and if allowed to occur would destroy the transistor in microseconds. D5 prevents the damage by becoming conductive and effectively shorting the relay coil. Do not be tempted to test this theory by omitting the diode unless you have a good supply of transistors!

Construction

A drilled, printed circuit board is available from Badger Boards but for the benefit of those wishing to prepare their own, the foil pattern is given in Fig 7.2.

The work has been arranged in a series of stages; each completes a part of the project which can be tested to check that it is working correctly. Fig 7.3 shows the position of the components on the PCB. This must be referred to continually to ensure that the components are inserted in the correct place. If you are using a commercial PCB there is probably a component indication on the component side. It is most important that constructors with little or no experience should not proceed to the next stage until satisfactory results are obtained from the tests on the section just completed. By following this method it will be much easier to see where a fault (if any) has occurred during the last few steps of the construction work.

If a fault does occur a check of the following should discover the cause. Examine the PCB very carefully for an accidental short-circuit caused by the use of too much solder. Use a solder sucker to remove the excess. Check the value of all components just fitted. In the case of diodes or transistors make sure that they are connected the right way round. Look for any dry joints which may leave a component unconnected. Remember – do not proceed until the stage just completed works correctly.

Preparing the board

1. Before any work is done on the board it should be laid in position, copper side down in the box in which the transmitter is to be installed. The position of the four fixing holes are marked. It is surprisingly difficult to get these in the correct place once the board is completed.
2. Insert the 25 pins in the positions indicated by a circle in the component layout diagram (see Fig 7.3). Methods of inserting pins are described in Appendix 1. The pins must be pushed down to the copper and then soldered using a medium-size bit (2 to 2.5mm) in the iron.
3. To avoid the need to change soldering iron bits later, T2 can be inserted. Ensure that the coil can is pushed down to the board, then the two larger can pins should be soldered.
4. Allow the iron to cool, then fit the smallest bit which should be used for the remainder of the work on the PCB.
5. Insert the three IC holders and solder. Take care as the pads are rather small. Do not insert the ICs yet. If the holders are marked with pin numbers or cut outs, fit them on the PCB so that pin 1 of the holder is located in the pads marked 1 on the board.

Stage 1

1. Insert and solder the following components: R1, R2, R3, R4, R5, C1, C2, C3, C4, C6, TR1 (carefully check the type and the position), crystals X1, 2, 3 and 4. Only one or two crystals need be fitted at this stage; others can be added later. Use position X1 if only one is to be fitted.
2. Use a short piece of wire to temporarily link pins S1 and 1.
3. Connect a 12V supply, positive to pin N (NET) and negative to pin 0V.
4. Use the RF probe and a low-voltage DC meter to measure the voltage at the end of R4 remote from the edge of the board. The clip on the flying lead of the probe should be connected to the 0V rail for all tests unless directed otherwise. The voltage registered should be in the region of 1 to 1.5V. This indicates that the crystal oscillator is working.

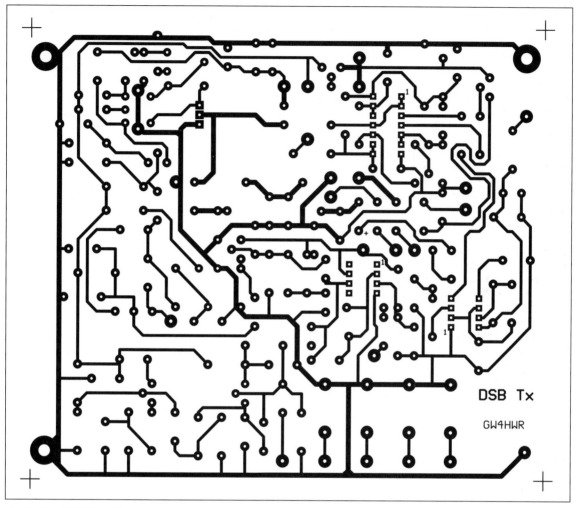

Fig 7.2. The PCB foil pattern

5. Test the voltage at the ends of C6 – this should be in the region of 0.5V.

6. If you have access to a cathode-ray oscilloscope (CRO) – a very simple one would be quite satisfactory – it could be used in the place of the RF probe and would allow you to see the waveform produced. The peak to peak voltage should also be about 1 to 1.5V. Because the RF probe uses a voltage doubler it also records peak-to-peak voltage. However, if no CRO is available don't worry as it is quite in order to do all of the testing using the probe and a multimeter.

7. Switch the power off.

Stage 2

The next stage is to wind T1. This is a very simple transformer with 10 turns of enamel-covered wire on both the primary and secondary. The secondary has a centre tap. Although simple the construction is quite fiddly and must be carried out with great care. The winding is made on a 'binocular' type ferrite core. Refer to Fig 7.4 and then examine the core. The ferrite material is very hard and often the inner edges of the holes are quite sharp. When the wire is passed through the holes these sharp edges have a nasty habit of scraping off some of the enamel covering and short-circuits can occur between turns or between the two windings.

To avoid this problem remove the sharp edges of the holes through the core by scraping with the point of a modelling knife, using the knife in a rotary motion. It will ruin the blade but it is worth the effort to get the holes smooth. See Fig 7.4(a). Check the results of your efforts by passing a short piece of enamel-covered wire through the holes and pulling it back and forward. If the insulation is being scraped off you should be able to feel a grating effect and examination of the wire will show where the insulation is damaged. Repeat the exercise with the knife until the wire runs smoothly through the holes. Don't proceed until this has been done.

Each winding will require about 400mm of 0.45mm (26swg). Maplin will supply wire in small reels of 50g which is much more than needed so that a second or third attempt is always possible. Wire from this source is insulated with an enamel which acts as a solder flux so that there is no need to scrape the covering off before soldering. The wire is said to be 'self-fluxing'.

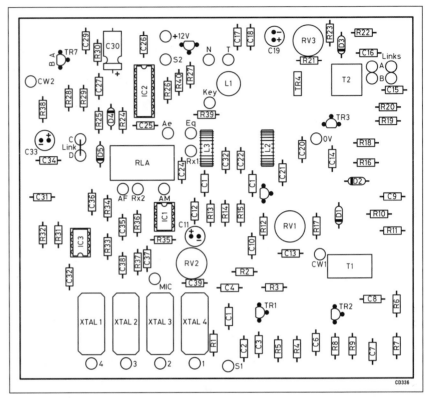

Fig 7.3. Layout of the components on the PCB

1. To reduce the possibility of damage, pass about half of the wire through one of the holes then back through the other hole as shown in Fig 7.4(b). This is one turn.
2. Now pass the two ends in turn through the holes, repeating the operation until 10 turns have been put on. Resist the temptation to pull the wire too tight – just enough to take up the slack. When complete both ends should be at one end of the core as in Fig 7.4(d).
3. Mark the centre of the second 400mm of wire by wiping the soldering iron bit over 20mm until the wire is completely tinned.
4. If the wire is insulated with a non-flux type of enamel the centre 20mm must be scraped to remove the insulation and then soldered.
5. Fold the wire in the centre of the soldered portion and twist gently together.
6. Solder to form a tap about 10mm long.
7. Pass the two ends through the two holes of the core so that the tap is at the end opposite to the leads from the primary winding as shown in Fig 7.4(e).
8. Now pass one of the long ends back through the core so as to produce one turn in one half of the secondary, then do the same with the other long end. You should have two wires and the centre tap at the end

of the core opposite to the primary leads with one turn on each half of the secondary.

9. Continue with each lead in turn until five turns have been wound on each half of the secondary and three wires are at one end of the core and two at the other end. Fig 7.4(f) shows the completed transformer.
10. Again pull the wires very gently to take up the slack but do not pull hard. The winding requires considerable concentration on the part of the constructor to ensure that the correct number of turns has been put on each section.
11. It is almost impossible to test the windings until the transformer is installed but a simple insulation test should be made by testing the resistance between the primary and the secondary. Strip the insulation from the end of one of the primary leads and one from the secondary.
12. Set the multimeter to the highest resistance range and check between the two bare ends. If all is well the meter should indicate at least $1M\Omega$ and often will show infinity (open-circuit). If a lower resistance is shown there is no alternative to stripping the wires from the core and winding again with new wire.
13. Check the edges of those holes through the core;

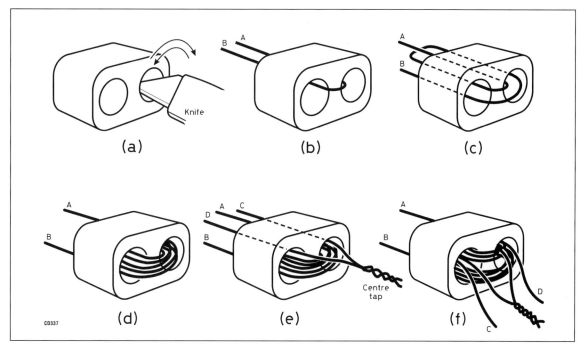

Fig 7.4. Winding transformer T1. (a) Remove the sharp edges from the holes. (b) The first turn is put on. Follow with A + B in turn. (c) Two turns. (d) Primary wound with 10 turns. (e) Start the secondary winding with the centre tap. (f) The completed transformer

almost every case of transformer failure is due to wire damage from the core.

14. Fit R6, R7, R8, R9, R10, R11, C6, C7, C8, C9, TR2 and finally T1. The three leads on one side of the transformer must pass through the three holes to the left of R11 with the tap going to the centre of the three.

15. The transformer can be fixed to the board by a small piece of double-sided sticky tape and later, if a more secure 'fix' is required, a spot of superglue can be put under the core.

16. Connect the 12V supply as in Stage 1 and link pins S1 and 1 if you have disconnected them.

17. Use the RF probe and DC meter to measure the voltage at the outside ends of the secondary of T1 – there should be about 1.5V at each point but, most importantly, the two voltages must be equal. If this test is satisfactory it is almost certain that the winding of T1 is OK.

18. Switch the power off.

Stage 3

1. Fit D1 and D2 with attention to the polarity – the mixer will not work if one of the diodes is reversed.

2. Fit RV1, R16, R17, R18, R19, C13 and C14.

3. Turn RV1 fully clockwise.

4. Apply power and use the RF probe to check the voltage at the junction of R18 and R19 – about 3V should be obtained.

5. Switch the power off.

Stage 4

1. Fit TR3, R20, C15 and C16.

2. Solder the remaining connections of T2 if not done when the coil was first fitted.

3. Fit link A – this can be a piece of tinned copper wire from the end of one of the components already fitted.

4. Apply power and test the voltage on the can of TR3 (collector), again using the RF probe. The voltage should be about 6V.

5. Using the special trimming tool (see Table 7.1), adjust the core of T2 for maximum voltage at the can of TR3. There is no need to be very precise at this stage as the core will need re-adjustment later.

6. Now adjust RV1 carefully for minimum voltage. It should be possible to reduce the voltage to zero.

7. Switch off the power and remove the positive supply lead from pin N.

Stage 5

8. Fit TR5, R12, R13, R14, R15, R35, R36, R37, RV2, C10, C11, C12, C37, C38 and C39.

9. Fit IC1, checking carefully on the position of the notch

at the end of the IC and on the layout diagram (Fig 7.3).

10. Connect the positive supply lead to pin AM. This will provide power to IC1 and TR5 only.

11. Solder two short pieces of insulated wire to pins 1 and 4 on the microphone socket to enable a temporary connection to be made to the microphone.

12. Connect the far end of the wire from pin 4 to 0V and the one from pin 1 to pin MIC on the PCB.

13. Switch the analogue meter to a low AC range and use ordinary leads (no probe) to connect between the junction of R10 and R11 with the other lead of the meter to 0V or ground.

14. Set RV2 to about mid-way.

15. Plug in a dynamic microphone (the type that is hand held and has a switch on the side), switch on the supply and speak or whistle loudly into the microphone. The meter reading should vary from 0V to about 1.5V.

16. Disconnect the positive supply lead from pin AM.

Stage 6

1. Wind L2 and L3. These are almost identical to those used in the 80m transmitter described in Chapter 5 with the only difference being the number of turns. Both coils require 26 turns of 0.56mm (24swg) enamel-covered wire on each ferrite ring. The method of winding is also identical so refer to Chapter 5 for the details of the construction.

2. Assemble TR4 and the heatsink. The flat surface of the transistor must be against the inside surface of the heatsink. Refer to Fig 7.5. Don't forget the dab of heatsink compound – if you do not have any, a little Vaseline is almost as effective but in any case don't use too much.

3. Fit RV3, R21, R22, R23, C17, C18, C19, C20, C21, C22, C23, C24, D3, L1, L2 and L3.

4. Turn RV3 fully anti-clockwise, connect the negative lead of the multimeter to pin T and the positive lead to the 12V supply, setting the meter to 100mA DC range. This will enable the current to the output stage to be measured.

5. Switch on the supply. The meter should register 20mA – this is the current through the bias network formed by R22 and RV3.

6. Carefully adjust RV3 until the current increases to 25mA, giving a standing collector current through TR4 of 5mA, enough to bring the transistor to the linear state.

7. Switch off the supply.

8. The output stage may be tested at this point. First a 50Ω dummy load must be connected. (If a proper load is not available a temporary one can be made by connecting two 100Ω 1W resistors in parallel. The

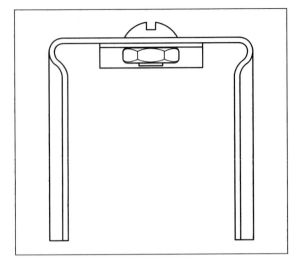

Fig 7.5. Fitting TR4 to the heatsink

combination should be soldered across C24 using the shortest leads possible.)

9. Leave the meter connected as in step 4 and connect pin N to the positive of the supply.

10. Temporarily link pin CW1 to 0V. Note that the supply must be capable of delivering more than 100mA.

11. Set the meter to a higher range (200mA or more) and switch on the supply. The meter should register between 120 and 150mA.

12. Connect the RF probe across the 50Ω dummy load with the crocodile clip on the flying lead connected to the earthy end. (Note that if you have only one meter it will be necessary to connect pins N and T together with the supply going to both pins.) The reading should be between 20 and 30V.

13. With the probe still in position, adjust the core of T2 (using the correct tool) to obtain a maximum reading from the probe.

14. Switch off the supply – it is possible that a very small amount of radiation will take place with the unit unboxed and the temporary dummy load in use, so do not leave on too long. Gently touch the dummy load resistors – they should be moderately warm, giving an idea of the power being delivered to the load.

If you have no intention of using this transmitter for CW, considerable time and expense can be saved by moving directly to Stage 9.

Stage 7

1. Insert the relay RLA1 – this is a small yellow box and the pins are so arranged that it will fit only one way. Ensure that it sits evenly on the board, then solder all eight pins.

Table 7.1. Components list

RESISTORS

R1	33k
R2	100k
R3, 16, 34	470R
R4	1k5
R5	1k8
R6, 18, 32	47k
R7, 13, 19, 22	6k8
R8	82R
R9, 20	150R
R10, 15	22k
R11, 31, 35	2k2
R12	330R
R14, 27, 29, 40	15k
R17, 23	220R
R21	33R
R24	820R
R25	3M9
R26	180k
R28	18k
R30, 38	56R
R33	1k0
R36, 37	10k
R39	100R

All fixed resistors are 0.25W carbon film.

RV1, 3	100R miniature horizontal preset
RV2	220k miniature horizontal preset

CAPACITORS

C1	100p

C2, 3, 16	150p
C4, 8, 18, 20, 25, 26, 31, 38	100n
C5	Not used
C6, 14, 17	1n0
C7, 9, 13, 15	10n
C10, 36, 37	4µ7 tantalum
C11, 33	10µ radial electrolytic
C12, 27, 35	470n layer type
C19	47µ radial electrolytic
C21–24	1n5 polystyrene
C30	22µ axial electrolytic
C32	22n
C39	4n

All capacitors are polyester or ceramic unless stated otherwise.

SEMICONDUCTORS

TR1, 2, 5	BC108 or BC548 or similar
TR3	BFY51
TR4	MRF475
TR6, 7	BC558 or similar PNP
D1–5	1N4148
IC1	741
IC2	4001B
IC3	NE555

INDUCTORS

T1	See text
T2	KANK3333 (TOKO)
L1	22µH (type 8RBS)
L2, 3	See text

MISCELLANEOUS

S1	3-pole 4-way rotary
S2	SPDT minature toggle
S3	DPDT minature toggle
RLA	TRK2233 Iskra (Maplin, Cirkit)
SK1	SO239 (single-hole fixing)
SK2	Phono (single-hole fixing)
SK3	DC power connector 2.5mm socket and plug
SK4	Microphone connector, four-way (or to suit available microphone)
X1–4	Any crystal in the range 1.85MHz to 1.99MHz (see text)

Trimming tool (Maplin, Cirkit)
Sockets for IC1, IC3 (8-pin DIL)
Socket for IC2 (14-pin DIL)
PL259 plug
Two phono plugs
6.3mm stereo jack plug
Two 6.3mm mono jack plugs
50g 24swg enamel-covered wire (Maplin, Cirkit)
50g 26swg enamel-covered wire (Maplin, Cirkit)
Heatsink type TV-5 (for TR4)
Heatsink type 5F (for TR3)
Two T68-2 iron toroids (for L2 and L3)
Binocular type core type A0004X030 twin-hole bead for T1 (Electrovalue)
PCB (Badger Boards)
Additional hardware items as detailed in Chapter 5 for the 80m CW transmitter.

---

2. Now fit R24, R25, R26, R27, R28, R29, R30, R39, R40, C25, C26, C27, C29, C30, D4, D5, TR6, TR7.
3. Insert IC2 into its socket.
4. Link Pins C and D.
5. Fit D4 and D5, ensuring that they are fitted the correct way round.
6. The switching circuitry can be tested by connecting the positive of the 12V supply to the +12V pin. Use a flying lead to connect pin K to 0V and listen for the relay operating. It should close immediately the connection is made but release after about two seconds when the connection is broken.
7. Connect a DC voltmeter between pin N and 0V. The meter should record 12 to 13V whenever pin K is shorted to 0V. This last test demonstrates that the supply to TR1, TR2 and TR3 is established whenever the key is pressed (or the PTT switch operated).

Stage 8

This is the sidetone circuit and is identical to the circuit used in the 80m CW transmitter.

1. Fit R31, R32, R33, R34, R38, C31, C32, C33, C34, C35 and C36. Insert IC3 into its socket, making sure that it is the right way round.
2. To test the circuit connect a supply as in Stage 7 and also to pin CW2.
3. Temporarily connect headphones to pin AF and 0V. Whenever pin K is connected to 0V the audio signal should be heard in the headphones.

Stage 9

This only applies if the transmitter is being built without the CW option.

1. Insert and solder the relay RLA.
2. Use a short piece of tinned copper wire (an offcut from a resistor) to link points A and B on the position allocated for TR7. The press-to-talk (PTT) switch will eventually be connected to the two pins C and D, which will not be linked and the supply to the transmitter will be provided by the redundant contacts on RLA. Details of these connections will be given at the end of the section describing the boxing-up process.

The Top Band transmitter PCB almost complete

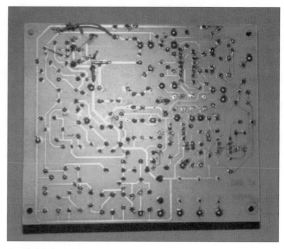

The PCB viewed from the track side

Installation of board

The board is now complete, has been tested and can now be installed in the case. It can be of a similar type to that used for the 3.5MHz transmitter described in Chapter 5 but with slightly different dimensions. It needs to be 20mm longer from back to front. Any commercial box having dimensions equal to or greater than those shown in Fig 7.6 would be suitable but it is felt that this would be a good opportunity to make up a box from 18 gauge sheet aluminium. To make the base requires only two 90° bends and the addition of two pieces of 12mm aluminium angle form flanges to enable the lid to be secured.

The arrangement is shown in Fig 7.6 and reference to Appendix 1 will provide information on bending and cutting.

The lid also needs only two 90° bends and can be made from either 18 or 20 gauge aluminium sheet. There are no flanges on the lid.

Note that although the position of the holes for the fixing screws to hold the lid is shown, the holes themselves must be marked through from the holes in the lid

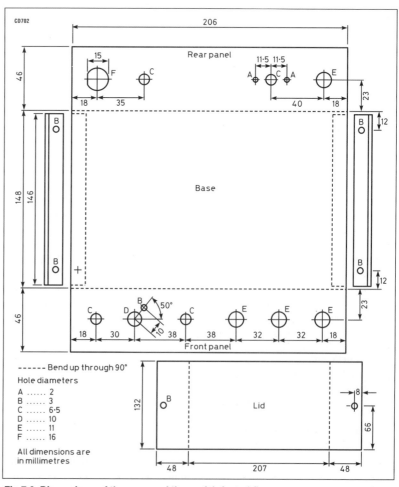

Fig 7.6. Dimensions of the case and the prefabricated flange

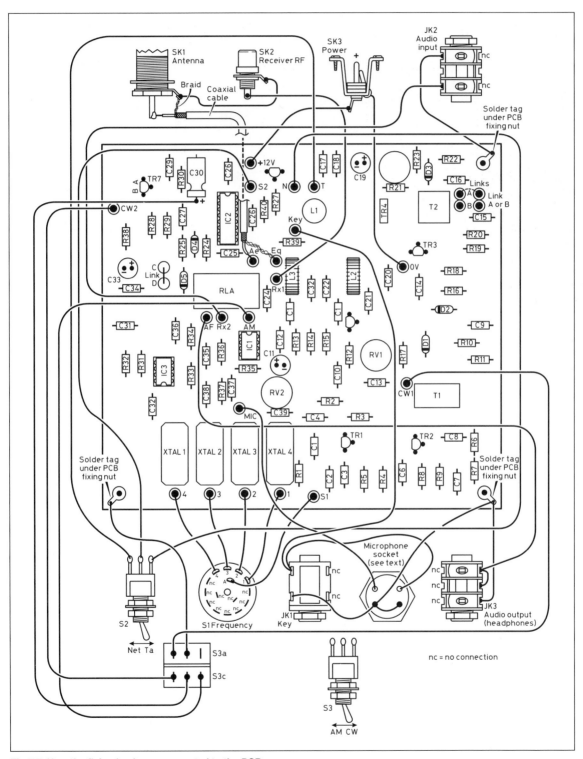

Fig 7.7. How the flying leads are connected to the PCB

The completed Top Band transmitter

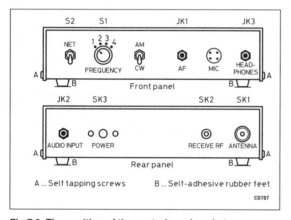

Fig 7.8. The position of the controls and sockets

after it has been made. The size of these holes will depend on the gauge of the self-tapping screws to be used. Test drillings in a piece of scrap angle should be made to ensure that the screws will cut their own thread without being too loose. If in doubt refer to the comments about screws in Appendix 1.

Owing to the complexity of the printed circuit foil pattern it was decided to rely on the metal case to provide the return (earth) path for most of the sockets. To enable this to be as efficient as possible, each of the four PCB fixing holes have been linked to the earth rail in the board. It is therefore most important that the PCB should be fixed

securely onto the base of the box before any tests other than those already described are made. Note also that solder tags are required at three of the fixing positions. These are placed under the nuts holding the board in place. The tags are shown in Fig 7.7.

The microphone socket must be chosen to suit the microphone which you intend to use. It is recommended that a simple dynamic type with a four-pin plug of the type used with some of the earlier transceivers from Trio and other manufacturers. These are available at low prices at radio rallies and possibly from club members. Test the pin connections by means of a multimeter switched to a low ohms range. The most common arrangement is for pins 1 and 4 to be connected to the microphone with pin 4 as the earthy end while pins 2 and 3 are connected to the PTT (press-to-talk) switch. This arrangement was assumed to be in use during the tests in Stage 5 which checked the AF amplifier. When the ohmmeter is connected between pins 1 and 4 a weak click should be heard from the microphone. If no click occurs, try all combinations of pins until one is heard. Test the resistance between pins 2 and 3 – it should be infinity until the PTT is pressed, when it should fall to zero.

Fig 7.7 shows how the various flying leads are connected. The microphone socket illustrated is the one described above. Follow the instructions in the diagram, cutting the leads so that they link the various pins with just a little to spare. The connection to the antenna socket must be made using coaxial cable. For those in doubt, details of the method of terminating coaxial cable can be found in Chapter 5.

Note the connections to S3 and follow the details in Fig 7.7 exactly. The method of connecting the microphone socket will depend on the microphone unit to be used.

If no CW option is to be used, the supply for TR1, 2 and 3 is provided by the contacts RLA2 on the relay during transmit. Connect pin N to pin AF and, on the copper side of the board, +12V to the pin marked '+' on the relay contacts.

Chapter 8

A frequency-modulated transmitter for 50MHz

FM transmitters can be quite simple in design and comparatively easy to construct, but they are rather difficult to set up after the construction is complete. This is brought about by the need to check the frequency output of the various stages, and therefore some frequency-checking device, capable of measuring up to 50MHz at least, is required. Ideally this would be a digital frequency meter but, as the cheapest new device is likely to cost about £100, it is worth looking at the goods on offer on the second-hand stalls at radio rallies as some very good instruments can sometimes be found. The author bought a meter which is capable of measuring frequencies up to 200MHz for about £30 at today's prices. It is quite old but is still giving excellent service. If you find a likely instrument get someone to test it for you before parting with the cash.

A 50MHz wavemeter

An alternative instrument will be described. It is very similar to the absorption wavemeter described in Chapter 2 but is dedicated to the bands involved in the transmitter to be described. It must be stressed that some form of frequency-measuring device is essential, and any attempt to set up the transmitter without such an instrument will result in the wrong output frequency which would almost certainly be outside the allocated 50MHz band.

If you do not possess a frequency meter it would be advisable to make the wavemeter probe before building the transmitter as it will enable each completed stage to be tested before continuing to the following one.

Circuit

The circuit diagram is shown in Fig 8.1 and will be seen to be very simple. It is almost the same as the one described in Chapter 2 but the construction

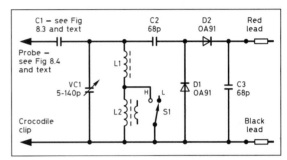

Fig 8.1. The circuit of the 50MHz wavemeter

is rather different. In use, it behaves as a crystal radio receiver with a very small antenna system and does not rely on energy being 'picked up' by absorption. This is necessary to ensure that the signal at given test points is being examined, as there will be at least four different frequency signals present in the completed circuit.

Construction

1. Cut the base board from a piece of copper laminate – preferably double-sided, although single-sided board can be used. In the latter case the components must be mounted on the copper side. The dimensions are given in Fig 8.2 and, apart from the holes for VC1,

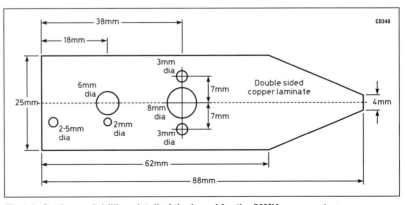

Fig 8.2. Cutting and drilling detail of the board for the 50MHz wavemeter

are not very critical. When cut and drilled the copper surface should be cleaned to make soldering easy.

2. Mount VC1 using two M2.5 screws which are no longer than 4mm. Details for fixing the capacitor are to be found in Chapter 3 and methods of cutting the screws (if too long) in Appendix 1. It is most important that VC1 be correctly fitted before any further construction is carried out. When satisfied, bolt the capacitor to the board and carry out a continuity check to ensure that the fixing screws have not shorted to the vanes of the capacitor.

3. Solder the centre pin of VC1 to the copper and bend up the right-hand pin (pins at the top of the capacitor) out of the way or cut it off, leaving about 1mm. Check with the layout in Fig 8.3.

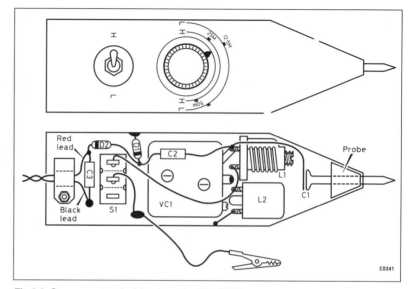

Fig 8.3. Component and wiring layout of the 50MHz wavemeter

4. Next prepare the actual probe. In the prototype this was made by cutting a plastic cable clip to the shape shown in Fig 8.4. Use a medium-size clip in which the fixing nail is about 20 to 25mm long. The plastic will cut quite easily using a sharp modelling knife. Any other method of supporting a short metal probe could be put to use.

5. Glue the probe assembly to the base as shown in Fig 8.3. Either superglue or quick-setting Araldite is satisfactory but in any case give plenty of time for the glue to set before going on to the next stage.

6. S1 can now be fitted. Note that if you have used double-sided board the switch will connect the two sides together so that there is no need for 'plating through'.

7. Solder L2 in position. The can is placed on the board so that one of its pins is lying on the copper and the marking ('3335R') is to the right-hand edge when

Table 8.1. Components list for the wavemeter

CAPACITORS
C1   See text
C2, 3   68p polystyrene
VC1   5–140p miniature variable capacitor (Maplin FT78K) with 6mm spindle extension piece and screw

INDUCTORS
L1   Type S18, 0.47µH (Cirkit/Maplin)
L2   TOKO KANK3335R 1.1µH (Cirkit/Maplin)

MISCELLANEOUS
D1, 2   Point-contact diode, OA91 or similar
S1   Miniature SPDT switch

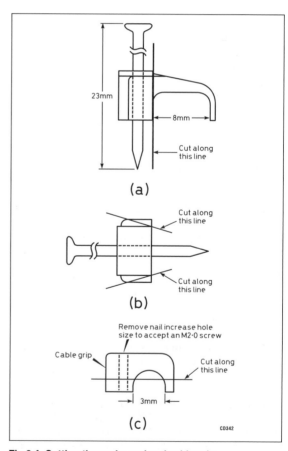

Fig 8.4. Cutting the probe end and cable grip

the pointed end of the board is away from you. As a double check, the three pins on one side of the coil should be in the approximate centre of the board. Bend the bottom pin gently so that it just touches the board and then solder the can pin and the lower of the three pins to the copper.

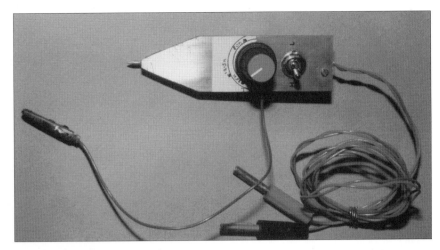

The RF probe viewed from the front

8. Examine L1 – you will see that there is a plastic rib along one side of the coil. Solder the pin of L1 on the opposite side to the rib, to the top pin of L2 and the other pin of L1 to the end tag of VC1. Adjust the position of the tag to suit.

9. C2 and D1 can now be fitted. Twist the leads from the red end of C2 and the cathode of D1 together so that there is about 3mm of lead between the end of the twist and each component. Solder the wires, making the joint as quickly as possible to avoid damage to the germanium diode.

10. Trim the other end of D1 to leave about 5mm, bend the join so that the two components are at right-angles, and solder the anode end of D1 to the board with C2 lying across the top of VC1.

11. Solder the free end of C2 to the junction of L1 and VC2. It will be necessary to wrap the wire around the solder tag of VC1 before soldering. At the same time wrap a second piece of wire (an offcut from a resistor will do) around the tag and then solder them all while holding L1 in position.

12. Bend the spare piece of wire so that the end lies close to the head of the nail forming the probe – it must not touch. The head of the nail and the wire forms C1.

13. D2 and C3 can now be connected together in the same way as D1 and C2 except that the plain end (not coloured) of C3 is connected to the cathode of D2. Reduce the free end of C3 to about 3mm and that of D2 to about 5mm.

14. Solder the anode of D2 to the junction of C2 and D1 and the free end of C3 to the copper of the board. Reduce the soldered joint between C3 and D2 to about 3mm.

15. Connect the centre pin of S1 to the copper board and the left-hand pin to the junction between L1 and L2.

16. Twist two pieces of PVC-insulated wire, one red and the other black or blue, together to form an output lead.

17. Fit red and black banana plugs to suit your multimeter to the ends of the lead and connect the other ends to the wavemeter; red to the junction of D2 and C3 and black to the copper of the board.

18. To prevent strain on the components during use, the lead should be held by some form of cable clamp. The prototype used a small electrical cable clip which was trimmed as shown in Fig 8.4. The hole will need to be enlarged to take a M2.0 or 8BA screw. When bolted up the cable should be held firmly.

19. Solder a short flying lead about 15mm long to the copper of the board as shown in Fig 8.3 and solder a small crocodile clip to the other end.

20. Fit a small pointer knob to the tuning control spindle and make a simple dial by drawing two semicircles on to a piece of white paper. The inner semicircle should be very slightly bigger than the control knob, with the second one about 2mm larger.

21. Paste the paper to the panel so that it is centred on the tuning spindle. Fig 8.3 shows the general idea. The calibration marks will be recorded on this dial later.

22. Set the two trimmers on the back of VC1 to minimum in order to give the maximum frequency coverage in the two ranges. The method of doing this is indicated in Fig 3.13 from Chapter 3.

Calibration

Now comes the hard part – the wavemeter must be calibrated. There are many ways of doing this but all involve some form of test equipment. A list of some of the possibilities follows in the hope that one of the methods will be suitable. All involve some form of calibrated signal source capable of providing signals from 13MHz to 50MHz:

- A signal generator.
- A low-power transmitter operating into a dummy load.
- A simple signal source such as the one described in Chapter 3.
- A dip meter.

The prototype was calibrated using a dip meter. This consists of an oscillator which has a number of plug-in coils and a meter which measures the grid or gate current of the valve or transistor forming the oscillator. If a tuned circuit having the same frequency as the oscillator is held close to the coil of the dip meter, the grid or gate current will fall as

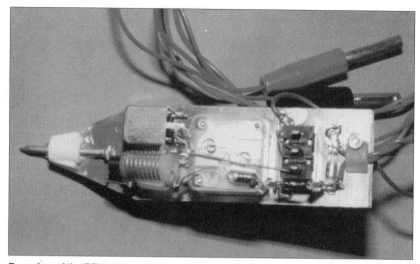

Rear view of the RF probe

energy is absorbed from the oscillator and will produce a 'dip' in the indicated meter reading.

1. Connect the leads of the probe to your multimeter which should be set to a low DC voltage range. Observe the correct polarity.
2. Insert the appropriate coil into the socket of the dip meter and switch on the supply.
3. Set the tuning control of the dip meter to 13MHz.
4. Set the range switch of the probe to the LOW position.
5. If the tip of the probe is held close to the coil of the dip meter while the probe tuning control is slowly rotated, a reading will be obtained on the multimeter when the probe and the dip meter have the same frequency.
6. Mark the position of the probe control on the front of the panel.
7. Repeat the process with the dip meter set to 25MHz. The probe should respond to this frequency on the LOW range with the probe tuning control almost at maximum.
8. Move the range switch to the HIGH position and find the position of the tuning control which provides an output.
9. Mark this position on the dial.
10. Repeat with the frequency of the dip meter set at 50MHz.

Frequency modulation

There are a number ways by which a carrier may be frequency modulated.

Method 1 – using a VFO

A variable frequency oscillator (VFO), similar to the oscillator used in the simple signal source described in

Chapter 3, can be used to generate a signal with the required output frequency. The frequency is determined by the values of the inductance (coil) and capacitance (capacitor) which form the oscillatory circuit. If a special type of capacitor known as a 'varicap diode' is connected in parallel with the oscillatory circuit, the frequency can be controlled by the audio frequencies from the microphone. The capacitance of the diode depends on the voltage applied to it – a higher voltage gives a lower value of capacitance and a low voltage a higher one. When the AF is applied to the diode, the frequency of the oscillator is changed in step with the audio frequencies.

A VFO operating at 50MHz will not maintain a constant output frequency (there will be frequency drift). To ensure that the output frequency of the oscillator remains constant (stable) it is often compared to the frequency of a crystal oscillator using what is known as a 'phase-locked loop'. This is a little difficult to set up and, if the circuit 'goes out of lock', the frequency of the oscillator may take up a value which is outside of the amateur band in use. Even if the frequency remains within the band, serious interference could be caused to other amateur stations. However, the system has the great advantage of being able to generate an unlimited number of frequencies within the band.

Method 2 – combined VFO and crystal oscillators

If a VFO covers a range of frequencies a little greater than the range required by the transmitter but operates at a much lower frequency, a relatively stable output can be obtained. To generate a stable carrier of the correct frequency (in this case about 50MHz), the output of the VFO is mixed with the output of a crystal oscillator. For

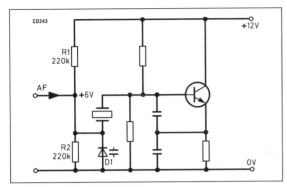

Fig 8.5. A crystal oscillator with a varicap diode as a control device. R1 and R2 form a high-impedance voltage divider to reverse-bias the diode D1. The AF input causes this bias to change

example, if the output of the VFO is 1.5 to 2.0MHz and the crystal oscillator is 48.5MHz, the sum frequencies will be variable from 50 to 50.5MHz. The output will be sufficiently stable and the VFO can be frequency modulated as described in Method 1. Again, the advantage of the system is the ability to be adjusted to any frequency within the prescribed range.

It sounds easy, but there are a number of problems with the successful construction of a stable VFO even at low frequencies.

Method 3 – a crystal oscillator

The frequency of a crystal oscillator can be changed by a few hertz (about 300 to 400Hz is a realistic amount) when the value of the capacitor connected to the crystal is changed. The maximum variation in the frequency of the carrier for FM in the amateur bands should be in the order of 2.5 to 3.0kHz.

Fig 8.5 shows how a varicap diode can be connected in a crystal oscillator circuit. The capacitance of the diode is determined by the voltage applied to it but the diode must at all times be biased to the non-conductive state by a DC voltage provided by the resistors R1 and R2. This steady voltage is varied by the audio frequency AC voltage from the AF amplifier and microphone. As the capacitance rises and falls, so the frequency of the crystal oscillator decreases and increases, but only by a maximum of about 400Hz.

To get a bigger change, the frequency chosen for the oscillator is much lower than the required output value, and a system of frequency

multiplication is used to increase it to the required output value. The block diagram in Fig 8.6 shows a very simple system in which three frequency multipliers are used to increase the frequency of the carrier by eight times. As the frequency is increased, so the amount that it changes increases. By multiplying by eight times the change (known as 'deviation') is also increased by a factor of eight. If the frequency of the crystal oscillator can be changed by 300Hz then the output frequency would change by 300×8 which equals 2400Hz (2.4kHz). This is small but it is most important that the deviation should not exceed 3kHz. If the frequency of the oscillator changes by 400Hz then the output deviation would be 3.2kHz. This is not likely to occur very often and should be acceptable.

Frequency multiplication of eight times is about the minimum practical value but some transmitters use 12 or even 18 times. With amateur transmitters it would then be possible to greatly exceed the permitted deviation of 3kHz.

Method 3 is used for the transmitter to be described with eight times multiplication of the crystal frequency.

The FM transmitter

Fig 8.7 shows the complete circuit diagram which is intended to indicate what the various sections do rather than how they do it. Don't worry about the way in which the circuit works but concentrate on the basic function. TR1 is a crystal oscillator very similar to those used in several projects already described except that it has a coil in the collector circuit which is tuned to the crystal frequency. This provides rather more radio frequency voltage than could otherwise be obtained and also allows the crystal frequency to be 'pulled' a little to bring the unmodulated output to an exact value. The crystal has a varicap diode connected in series with it instead of the ordinary capacitor used in the circuits described in earlier chapters.

As with the earlier transmitters, four crystals are switchable to allow for up to four channels. The recommended frequencies are 51.45MHz, 51.47MHz, 51.49MHz and 51.51MHz which is used as the calling

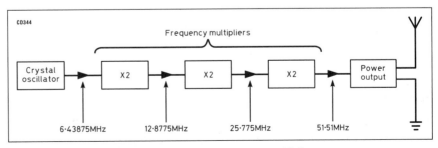

Fig 8.6. A block diagram of a transmitter with frequency multipliers

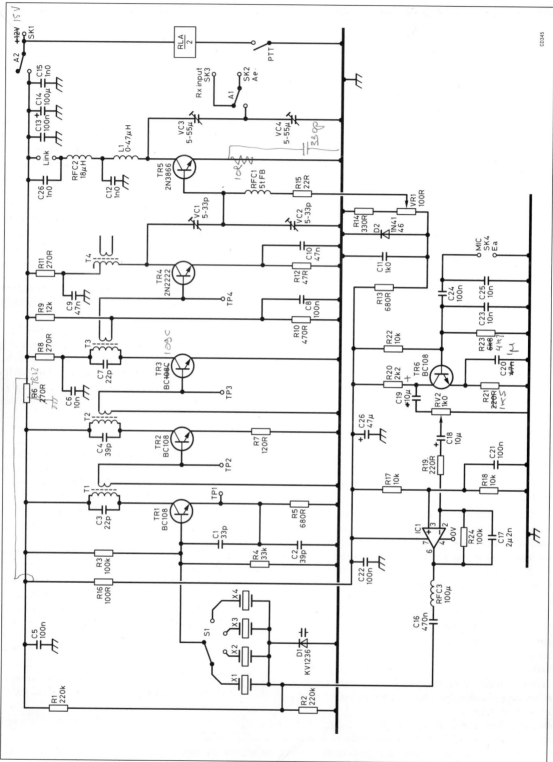

Fig 8.7. The circuit of the FM transmitter

channel. Crystals having frequencies of 6.43125MHz, 6.43375MHz, 6.43625MHz and 6.43875MHz will be required. Other frequencies could be used as long as they produce output frequencies within the allotted band, but it is important to keep them grouped close together to avoid tuning problems in later stages of the transmitter.

The output from the secondary winding of T1 is applied between the base and emitter of TR2 – the first frequency doubler. The transistor is not biased which means that with no signal applied there will be no current through it. Because TR2 is a silicon transistor there will be no current until the input voltage increases to about +0.6V. As explained in Chapter 4, this results in considerable distortion of the applied signal – in other words the output will contain harmonics of the input. The tuned circuit consisting of C4 and the primary of T2 is tuned to a frequency which is twice that of the crystal – the second harmonic. The circuit responds to the harmonic and not the fundamental and it is this signal which appears across the secondary of T2. R7 in the emitter circuit is included to prevent overloading of T2 by the rather large signal from the secondary of T1.

TR3 is the second frequency doubler and works in a similar way to TR2 but, because the signal present at the output of T2 is less than that from T1, no emitter resistor is needed. Again, distortion of the input signal will take place, and the tuned circuit consisting of C7 and the primary of T3 is tuned to the second harmonic. The output across the secondary of T3 will have a frequency of four times that of the crystal oscillator.

TR4 is similar except that a transistor more suitable for the higher frequencies has been used. It is more easily damaged by temperature rise which is likely to produce a result known as 'thermal runaway'. As the transistor warms up it passes more current and so gets even warmer, then passes yet more current – eventually it destroys itself. This effect is prevented by the resistor R12 in series with the emitter of the transistor which reduces the bias as the temperature rises. The resistor is called a 'stabilising resistor'. To prevent a reduction in gain due to negative feedback (out-of-phase voltage fed back to the input), C10 is connected in parallel with R12.

It is possible that the voltage from the secondary of T3 may not be big enough to cause TR4 to conduct. R9 and R10 apply a small positive voltage between the base and emitter of TR4. It is not enough to make the transistor conduct in the absence of any signal but has the effect of reducing the value of the input necessary. The output from the secondary of T4 is now eight times that of the crystal and is the frequency required for the output of the transmitter.

The voltage fed to the base of TR5 is not taken from the secondary of T4 because it is necessary to provide some matching; this is provided by VC1 and VC2 which

effectively give a variable tap on the capacitor across the primary of T4.

TR5 is the output transistor which is easily capable of 500mW; with careful setting up it will provide an output of just about 1W. The output impedance will be in the order of 100 to 50Ω so that the matching is relatively simple. The matching circuit is formed by VC3, L1 and VC4. The transistor is operated in Class AB1 mode (it is biased so that it is just conductive with no signal applied). This results in less harmonic distortion and reduces the chance of harmonic radiation. The mode also requires less input for a given output but is not quite so efficient. Bias is provided by R13, RV1 and R14, with D2 stabilising the bias voltage so that it is not effected by changes in supply voltage. The link between the supply rail and RFC2 enables the collector current to be monitored while the bias voltage is adjusted. The RF output is fed to the antenna when the relay RLA is energised by the press-to-talk switch. The other contacts on the relay are used to switch on the transmitter.

The microphone amplifier is quite conventional with one transistor (TR6) stage followed by a high-gain operational amplifier (IC1). Attenuation of the lower audio frequency is by the use of low-value coupling capacitors and attenuation of high frequency (above 3kHz) by input capacitors C25 and C23 and the use of selective negative feedback in the integrated circuit provided by C17. The output from the amplifier is fed via RFC3 and C16 to the varicap diode (D1), varying the frequency of the crystal oscillator in step with the audio frequencies.

Construction

As with the two previous transmitters, most of the components are mounted on a printed circuit board. For those wishing to etch their own board the foil pattern is given full size in Fig 8.8. The board is double sided with the plain copper side being used as a ground plane. Clearance must be provided around all of the holes with the exception of those where the component is connected to ground. A foil pattern to produce the clearance spots is shown full size in Fig 8.9. An alternative method, which is rather more time consuming, involves cutting the copper around each hole (on the plain side) using either a spot face cutter or a small twist drill. Both tools are used by hand – not in a hand drill. Avoid removing the copper around those holes which are used for ground connections. Fig 8.9 could assist in this rather laborious task.

Note that all components which have one end connected to the 0V rail (chassis) should have the earthy end soldered to both the pad on the track side of the PCB and the ground plane on the component side. The copper has not been removed from around these holes in the ground plane.

1. Start the construction by inserting the 15 terminal

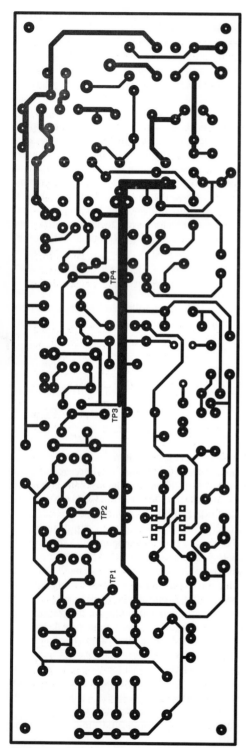

Fig 8.8. The PCB foil pattern – full size

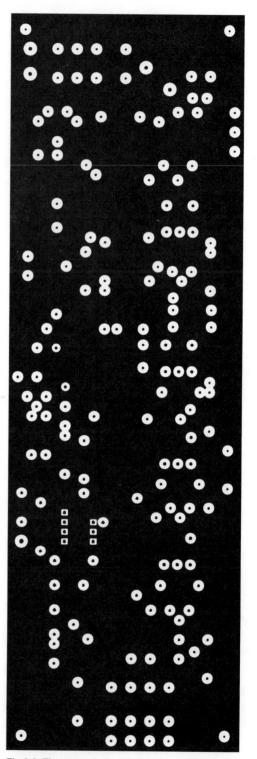

Fig 8.9. The ground plane foil pattern – full size

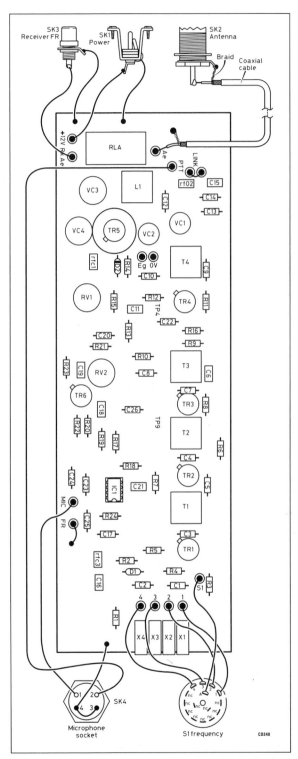

Fig 8.10. Component layout and connection of flying leads

pins indicated on the board or on the layout in Fig 8.10 in the positions marked with a circle. If you are using a board which does not have the components marked on the component side you should keep referring to the layout shown in Fig 8.10. The pins should be inserted from the track side of the PCB and soldered.

2. If you have 'plating through' pins, four of these should be inserted in the holes marked 'TP1', 'TP2', 'TP3' and 'TP4'. If none are available, use four single-ended pins instead. These four pins are inserted from the component side of the PCB and soldered on the track side. The heads of the pins form the test points. Note that the positions for these last four pins are not marked with a circle on the layout and the position must be found by referring to the 'TP1' etc marking on the track side of the board.

3. Fit the five resistors R1 to R6; all have been allowed 10mm spacing so that if the leads are bent at right-angles to the resistor body the components will lie flat against the board.

4. Fit the capacitors C1, C2, C3 and C5.

5. Fit D1, the varicap diode, with the markings facing away from the crystal position. Note that the diode comes as a dual package and needs to be carefully cut into two. It is a fairly expensive component so it may be worth looking for another constructor who is interested in the other half.

6. Fit the four crystals so that they stand about 2mm above the board. It is recommended that the 'calling channel' crystal (6.43875MHz) be fitted in position 1 with the others in order of frequency. This is a matter of personal choice and any order can be used, but remember that the frequencies of the group of crystals should cover the minimum range or there could be problems with tuning in the final set-up.

7. Fit TR1 with not more than 4mm clearance from the board. Check the orientation from Fig 8.10.

8. To complete this section fit T1 (TKANS32696A – white) so that it sits right down on the board. The can pins (the flat ones) must be soldered to the pads on the track side of the board. Probably it will not be possible to solder to the ground plane as the copper may have been removed from around the hole.

9. This section may now be tested but don't worry about exact frequencies at this stage. Temporarily fit a positive supply lead to the LINK pin nearest to C15 (not yet fitted) and a negative lead to any convenient point on the copper ground plane.

10. Short pin S1 to pin 1; a resistor lead offcut will do for this temporary connection.

11. Connect a 12V supply.

12. With the diode probe flying lead connected to the

ground plane, check for a voltage at TP2. The multi-meter should be set to a low DC voltage range.

13. Using the correct trimming tool (see later), adjust the core of T1 for maximum output. This should be in the order of 4V and the voltage at TP1 about 2V. Note: there will not necessarily be any voltage at TP1 until after the core of T1 has been adjusted.

14. When the tests have been satisfactorily made switch off the supply.

15. Continue with the construction by fitting R7, C4, TR2 and T2 which is a KANK3334R (yellow).

16. Switch on the supply and use the probe to test the voltage at TP3 while adjusting the core of T2. This voltage should be about 1V. It is most important that the correct tool be used for this purpose as a small screwdriver will almost certainly crack the core and it may be impossible to remove the broken pieces. Even if the worst does not happen, the presence of a steel blade will upset the tuning operation and even the brass end of a professional tool may have some effect. With a little patience a suitable trimming tool can be made from a short piece of thin plastic knitting needle – about 1.5mm diameter and 50mm long would be ideal. Use a fine, sharp file to produce a screwdriver end which will fit into the slot in the end of the core of the coils.

17. Replace the RF probe with the 50MHz wavemeter and carefully tune its control; a frequency of just about 12.5MHz should be indicated.

18. Again switch off the supply and proceed with the construction.

19. Fit R8, R9 and R10 followed by C6, C7, C8, C13, C15 and C14, observing the polarity of this electrolytic capacitor.

20. Fit TR3 (note that this must be a BC108C in order to get sufficient drive to the next stage).

21. Fit T3 which is a KANK3335R (pink).

22. With the supply on, test the voltage at TP4 while adjusting the core of T3 – a value of about 1V should be obtained.

23. A further test with the wavemeter should reveal a frequency of about 25MHz.

24. Fit R11, R12, C9, C10, VC1 and VC2.

25. Fit TR4 in the same way as the previous transistors but take care to avoid overheating while soldering.

26. Fit T4, which is the same type as T3 (pink).

27. Set VC1 near to its maximum value by looking at the position of the vanes and adjusting so that about a quarter of the moving vanes are visible.

28. Similarly set VC2 so that three-quarters of the vanes can be seen. Don't worry about getting this exactly right as the capacitors will be adjusted later.

29. Switch on the supply and check the voltage with the

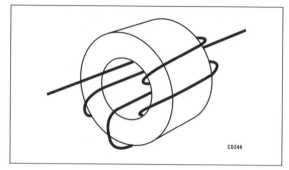

Fig 8.11. Winding RFC1

RF probe at the adjustment screw of VC1 (that is, the junction between VC1 and VC2).

30. Adjust the core of T4 for maximum voltage; about 1.5V should be obtained and the wavemeter should indicate 50MHz.

31. The remaining components in the RF section of the transmitter can now be fitted. Fit R13, R14, R15 and R16, RV1, D2 (check the polarity), C11, C12 and C26.

32. RFC1 is made by winding five turns of enamel-covered wire on to a small ferrite bead, keeping the turns spaced around the bead (see Fig 8.11). The choke is then fitted close to the PCB. Don't forget to remove the enamel from the wire before soldering if self-fluxing wire has not been used.

33. L1 is a type S18 moulded coil with an inductance of 0.470µH and is fitted so that it sits down on the PCB.

34. RFC2 is fitted in the same way.

35. VC3 and VC4 have been allotted two different fixing positions to cater for the two types of trimmer available. They differ only in the position of the 'earth' pins.

36. Use a short piece of tinned copper wire to make the short link next to R10.

37. Fit TR5 so that it sits about 3mm above the PCB.

38. Attach a heatsink to TR5. The heatsink is expanded by pushing the end of a screwdriver into the slot. Put a tiny dab of heatsink compound or Vaseline on the can of the transistor and then gently put the heatsink in position with the bottom edge of the heatsink touching the rim of TR5.

39. Set RV1 fully anticlockwise and connect a DC milliammeter between the two pins marked 'LINK' just above RFC2.

40. The positive lead of the meter should be connected to the pin being used as supply positive and the negative lead to the other pin. This meter is now able to monitor the current being passed by TR5.

41. Set the meter range to 100mA.

42. Remove the core from L1 but put it in a safe place in

case it is needed later and, if you have not already done so, fit the screening can over L1.

43. Set VC3 so that the vanes are almost completely enmeshed and VC4 about half-way.

44. RF power transistors can be quite easily damaged by mismatch, both at the input and the output, and a dummy load is essential to allow the transistor to be correctly matched and also to prevent excessive radiation. Connect two 100Ω 1W carbon or carbon film resistors in parallel and solder them temporarily across VC4 on the print side of the PCB.

45. Before doing the following tests, recheck all of the points in step 31 onwards and then, when you are sure everything is correct, switch on the supply. Be sure that you are able to switch off quickly if necessary. While doing the tests, always watch the milliammeter and keep checking the temperature of the transistor. It is quite in order to monitor the temperature with your finger – there is no danger of shock and very little chance of getting burnt.

46. With the RF probe on the screw adjuster of VC4, adjust VC1 and VC2 for maximum output. This is not a simple 'one off' operation as there are many settings of the two controls which will give a maximum.

47. Note the value of the reading, alter the setting of VC1 slightly and readjust VC2, again noting the value – if it is higher than before, move VC1 a little more in the same direction. If the reading is lower, VC1 was moved in the wrong direction.

48. Again readjust VC2.

49. Keep doing these operations until the best maximum is obtained.

50. Now go through the same process using VC3 and VC4 – this time it is most important to keep watching the meter which is measuring the current through TR5. When this reaches a value of about 120mA be very careful as the output is in the region of 0.75W.

51. Replace the RF probe with the 50MHz wavemeter and set it to the mark you have made for 50MHz.

52. Adjust the control *very carefully* for a maximum value. If the control is very close to the 50MHz mark it is likely that the output frequency is correct but it must be stressed that with any transmitter using multipliers there is a very good chance that the output of any multiplier stage could be at the wrong frequency. Although the wavemeter if correctly calibrated gives a good indication, every effort should be made to get the use of a frequency meter when the final setting up is carried out. As an example of the problem, take a crystal frequency of 6.25MHz (value chosen to keep the arithmetic simple), double it and we have 12.5MHz, double it again and the output becomes 25MHz. If the second doubler becomes a tripler due

Table 8.2. Components list for the FM transmitter

RESISTORS

R1, 2	220k
R3, 24	100k
R4	33k
R5, 13	680R
R6, 8, 11	270R
R7	120R
R9	12k
R10	470R
R12	47R
R14	330R
R15	22R
R16	100R
R17, 18, 22	10k
R19, 21	220R
R20	2k2
R23	6k8
RV1	100R
RV2	1k0

CAPACITORS

C1	33p
C2	39p
C3, 7	22p silver mica or polystyrene
C4	33p silver mica or polystyrene
C5, 8, 13, 21, 22, 24	100n
C6, 23, 25	10n
C9, 10, 20	47n
C11, 12, 15	1n0
C14	100µ radial electrolytic
C16	470n layer type
C17	2n2
C18, C19	10µ tantalum
C26	47µ
VC1, 2	3–35p
VC3, 4	5–65p

INDUCTORS

T1	Toko TKANS32696A (white)
T2	Toko KANK3334R (yellow)
T3	Toko KANK3335R (pink)
T4	Toko KANK3335R (pink)
L1	Style S18 0.47µH and screening can
RFC1	5 turns on a ferrite bead
RFC2	Style 8RBS 18µH
RFC3	Style 7BS 100µH

SEMICONDUCTORS

TR1, 2, 6	BC108
TR3	BC108C
TR4	2N2222
TR5	2N3866
D1	Varicap diode – half KV1236
D2	1N4146
IC1	µA741

MISCELLANEOUS

SK1	DC power connector 2.5mm plug and socket
SK2	SO239 socket, single-hole fixing
SK3	Receiver input socket, phono single-hole fixing
SK4	Microphone input socket, 4-way
X1–4	See text

IC holder, DIL-8
Heatsink type 5f
Relay, minature type Iskra TRK2233

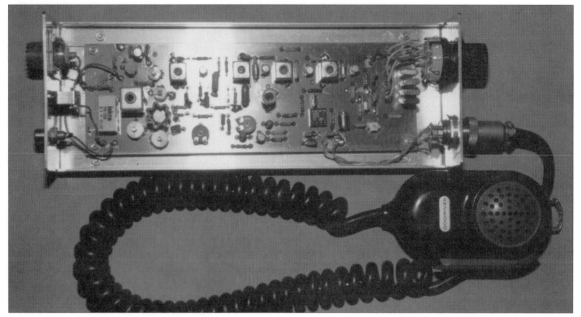

The 50MHz transmitter board installed in its box

to mistuning, then the output of this stage will be 37.5MHz and from the third doubler there will be an output of 75MHz – the wavemeter should be capable of indicating that this has occurred. However, if two stages each triple, an input of 6.25MHz would emerge as 56.25MHz – possibly close enough to 'fool' the wavemeter but providing an 'out-of-band' signal if the last stage acts as a simple amplifier with no doubling.

53. TR5 is working in Class C at the moment so there will be considerable harmonics in the output. To correct this TR5 must be operated in Class AB1 mode. Switch off the supply and remove the temporary link from pin S1 to 1. This will stop the oscillator and there should be no drive available on TR5 base.

54. Switch on the supply and note the meter reading – it should be zero. To be certain reduce the meter range to 5 or 10mA.

55. If all is well adjust RV1 slowly, monitoring the meter current constantly. If you are unable to read any current at any setting of RV1 check that you have inserted the link close to R10. Continue turning RV1 clockwise until the indicated current becomes 1.5mA. TR5 is now in the linear mode.

56. Switch off the supply, reconnect pins S1 and 1 and switch on again.

57. Use the RF probe connected as before to the adjusting screw of VC4 and note the reading. It should be in the order of 20 to 25V which corresponds to about 1W.

58. Now go through the circuit stage by stage, starting at TP2, using the RF probe and the 50MHz wavemeter in turn (the wavemeter cannot respond to the output from TP2 as the frequency is too low at this point). Adjust the core of T1 for maximum output.

59. Move to TP3, adjust the core of T2 for maximum on the RF probe and then check the frequency using the 50MHz wavemeter; at this point the frequency should be about 12.5MHz.

60. Move to TP4 and adjust the core of T3, checking both voltage and frequency, which should be 25MHz at this point. Note that when the transmitter is boxed up and the flying leads connected it will be necessary to repeat these checks and adjustments to ensure that all stages perform correctly with all four crystals.

61. The transmitter has now been operating for some time, so check the temperature of the heatsink of TR5; it should be quite warm but not too hot to touch. The two 100Ω resistors being used as a dummy load should also be moderately warm.

62. If you have a receiver capable of working on 50MHz in FM mode, the presence of a carrier will be indicated by the background noise disappearing as the squelch comes into operation.

63. At this stage you could make use of a domestic FM receiver tuned to about 100MHz. Place the receiver or its antenna as close as possible to L1 and carefully tune the receiver. As the transmitter is not modulated you should listen for a reduction in the background noise. If a clear indication of signal occurs it suggests

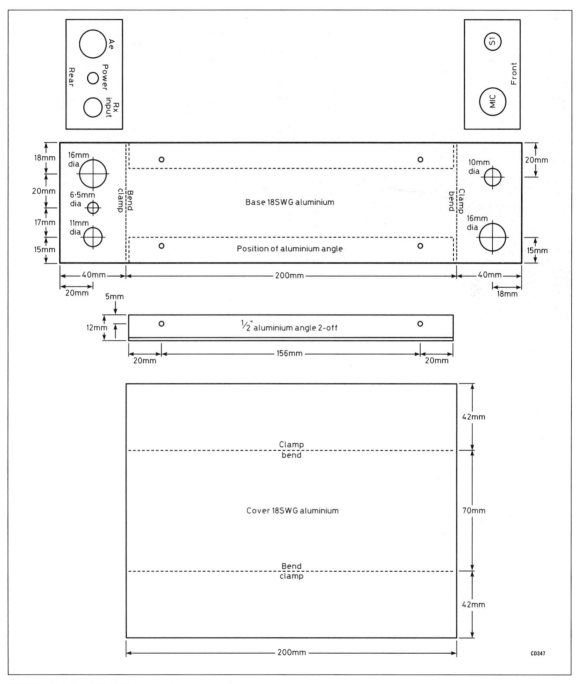

Fig 8.12. Details of the home-made box

that there is a second harmonic present and retuning of the output stages must be carried out. This test can be repeated later when there is a modulated signal.

64. The AF amplifier can now be completed and tested. Fit the IC holder for IC1 and follow with resistors R17, R18, R19, R20, R21, R22, R23, R24 and RV2, and capacitors C16, C17, C18, C19, C20, C21, C22, C23, C24 and C25.

The completed 50MHz transmitter

65. Fit RFC3, which is a small, white, plastic package with '101J' marked on top.
66. Mount TR6 as before, about 3mm above the surface of the board.
67. Plug in IC1, making sure that the notch at one end is in the position indicated in Fig 8.10.
68. Connect the microphone socket, using temporary leads to the pins MIC and EA.
69. Set RV2 at about mid-way.
70. Disconnect the meter from the link pins next to RFC2 to disable TR5 and connect it between RFC3 (either end) and the ground plane.
71. Set the meter to the lowest AC voltage range.
72. Plug in the microphone, switch on the supply and speak fairly loudly into the microphone. The meter (which should preferably be an analogue type) will provide an output which changes in time with your voice.
73. If this test is satisfactory, switch off the supply, link the pins next to RFC2 and switch on again.
74. Set the FM receiver to the appropriate frequency (51.51MHz) and speak into the microphone. You should be able to hear your own voice but it will probably sound strange as there will be some acoustic feedback between the receiver loudspeaker and the

transmitter microphone. Headphones will eliminate this effect.

75. Turn RV2 clockwise while continuing to talk; you will probably be able to move it to maximum without causing any ill effects. Note all these tests must be made with the dummy load in place – *do not use an antenna of any sort.*
76. When satisfied that everything is working correctly, fit the relay and remove the various temporary leads.

Fitting in the box

Boxing up is relatively simple and any metal box measuring $200 \times 70 \times 40$mm or larger will do. The dimensions for a home-made box are given in Fig 8.12. There are only four sockets and one switch to be accommodated so that the wiring up is also simple. Follow the layout shown in Fig 8.10, modifying where necessary to suit the box used if you have not made your own. If your microphone has a press-to-talk switch, use the layout shown. If not, the microphone can be connected by means of a two-pin plug and socket, and the antenna relay operated by means of a simple switch which should be labelled 'Send/Receive'.

The transmitter should be used with a dipole antenna having an impedance of 50Ω or be used with a suitable antenna tuning unit. A 50MHz dipole is included in the RSGB book *Practical Antennas for Novices.*

Chapter 9

Transmitters and test equipment for the 1.3GHz band

The Novice microwave bands

Two microwave bands are included in the UK Novice Licence Schedule. More bands may be included at a later date. The present bands are the 1.3GHz (sometimes known as the '23cm' or 'L' band) and the 10GHz ('3cm' or 'X') band. These two bands are very different!

You will find that building simple, low-power transmitters for the Novice microwave bands is in some ways similar to the transmitters already described for the lower frequency bands and in other ways very different! It is as well to talk a little about the bands and the similarities and differences before we go on to describe some practical designs for the two bands because they, too, are very different.

Most of the amateur microwave bands are 'Secondary, shared' allocations, which means that there are Primary (professional) users who have priority over amateur users. The main Primary uses for many of the microwave bands are radio location and direction finding (radar), fixed/mobile services, point-to-point commercial digital/data/telephone links and 'industrial, scientific and medical' (ISM) use.

Because both bands are much wider than the lower frequency bands (the 23/24cm band is 85MHz wide in the UK and the 3cm band is 500MHz wide) and are shared with other users, we need to divide the bands in to sub-bands or smaller 'segments'. In any case it would be difficult to tune over the whole of the bands in order to find other amateur stations to work. Also, most microwave stations will use very high gain antennas so that the transmitter power is concentrated into a narrow beam, which makes the transmitter more effective when the beam is pointed towards the station to be worked.

For these reasons, it is very important to stick to the bandplans which are designed to tell you where to find different kinds of transmissions and to avoid interference to, and from, the other band users.

Amateur transmitters and receivers in the microwave bands use either wide-band (WB) or narrow-band (NB) modulation. Narrow-band signals may have a bandwidth of a few 100Hz (CW), 2.5 to 3kHz for SSB or 5kHz to 7kHz for narrow-band FM (NBFM). By contrast, wide-band FM (WBFM) might have a bandwidth of between 50 and 250kHz and a fast-scan FM television (FMTV) signal might need 25MHz.

The 1.3GHz bandplan

The bandplan for the 1.3GHz band is given in Fig 9.1. 'All mode' operation is shown between 1256MHz and 1260MHz, 1286MHz and 1291MHz, and 1291.5MHz to 1296MHz. 1291MHz to 1291.5MHz is used for NBFM repeater inputs, the repeater outputs being between 1297MHz and 1297.5MHz. 1241MHz to 1256MHz and 1270MHz to 1286MHz are used for fast-scan TV (FSTV) and TV repeater inputs, while the segment 1300MHz to 1325MHz is used for FSTV and TV repeater outputs. TV, of course, uses WB modulation, either AM or FM. FMTV is used more than AM, since it is easier to use.

The part of the band used for NB communication (international speech and CW) lies between 1296MHz and 1298MHz. This part of the band is used worldwide for NB transmissions, with the 'centre of activity' (SSB) on 1296.2MHz. One area for Novice NBFM transmissions is between 1297.5MHz and 1298MHz, which is shown as 'FM simplex', although there is no reason why frequencies between 1296.3MHz and 1296.8MHz should not be used for NBFM and attended personal callsign beacon transmitters. The frequencies between 1298MHz and 1300MHz are kept specially for remote control and fixed data links.

The 10GHz bandplan

The bandplan for the 10GHz band is given in Fig 9.2. There is less detail in this bandplan partly because it is a very wide band and does not need such detailed planning, partly because the power used and the distances covered are less than at lower frequencies, and partly because very narrow antenna beams (dish antennas) are used by both amateur and professional users of the band. All these things mean that frequencies can be re-used (without interference) over smaller distances than in the

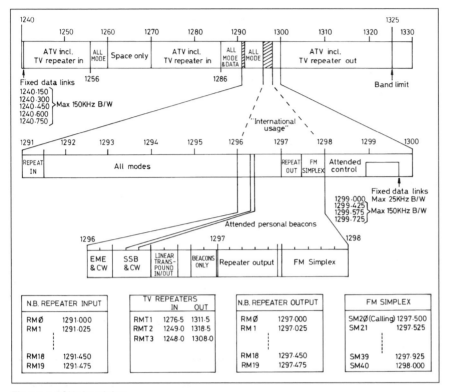

Fig 9.1. 1.3GHz bandplan

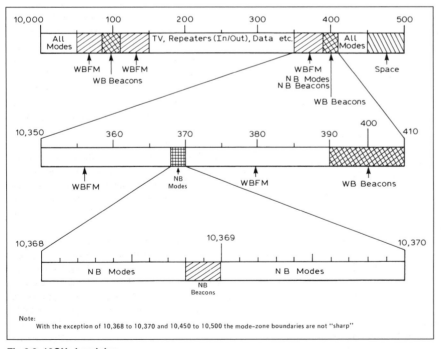

Fig 9.2. 10GHz bandplan

other bands. It also means that it doesn't matter too much if there is some overlap in the sub-bands.

10,000 to 10,050MHz and 10,410 to 10,450-MHz are 'all-mode' segments and include both data and FSTV. 10,050 to 10,150MHz and 10,350 to 10,410MHz are used for WBFM speech and frequency-shift or audio frequency-shift keyed (FSK/AFSK) transmissions, including WB beacons. By 'WB' we mean signals with a modulated bandwidth of 50 to 250kHz or more. In this band, WB signals are usually generated by transmitters which are *not* crystal controlled. There are three pairs of TV repeater channels at 10,200/10,040MHz, 10,225/10,065MHz and 10,250/10,150MHz. Narrow-band transmitters use the segment 10,368 to 10,370MHz, including NB beacons: this segment is used internationally. The segment between 10,150-MHz and 10,350MHz includes FSTV, TV and speech repeaters and data. The frequencies between 10,450MHz and 10,500MHz are used for space and satellites. You can see that much of the band is used for WB transmissions.

Again, it is a good idea to stay with the bandplan and operate around the frequencies which are used most, because there you are more likely to find other amateurs to

Fig 9.3. (a) Block diagram of a multiplier-type microwave transmitter source (frequencies in megahertz in brackets), showing interstage bandpass filters. (b) Block diagram of a low-power transmitter using the multiplier source of (a) with an amplifier to boost the power output

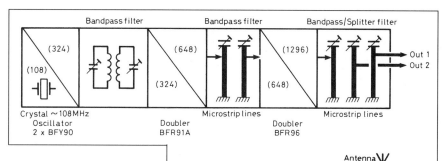

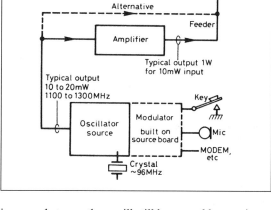

work. At the moment, most wide-band operation takes place between 10,370MHz and 10,400MHz.

Microwave transmitter design

Oscillators

As with the lower-frequency transmitters already described, every microwave transmitter starts off with an oscillator which usually (but not always) generates a frequency much lower than the operating frequency. This is because it is easier to design and build a stable oscillator at lower frequencies than it would be at the higher output frequency.

For example, a crystal oscillator rather than a variable frequency oscillator (VFO) is more often, but not always, used for microwave transmitters. You can easily get overtone crystals from about 80 to 120MHz and these are not expensive. Although higher-frequency crystals are made, they are easily damaged and very expensive.

Use of frequency multipliers

As we have seen, it is quite common to start in this range and then multiply the frequency, often in several stages, to the final working frequency. A simple low-power microwave transmitter diagram might look something like the block diagram, Fig 9.3, which is a transmitter for the 1.3GHz (23cm) band. The crystal oscillator gives an output at three times the crystal frequency. If the crystal used is at 108MHz, then the output is at 324MHz. This is followed by a doubler stage to 648MHz, and then by another doubler stage to 1296MHz, which is where the output is wanted.

The importance of filters
Because the starting frequency is quite low and several stages of multiplication are used, there are several sub-harmonics (frequencies *below* the output frequency) and harmonics (frequencies *above* the output frequency) present in the transmitter. It is very important that we use filters to remove all the unwanted frequencies which are present.

The tuned circuits between stages are bandpass filters which filter out most of the unwanted sub-harmonics but, because we have multiplied the original crystal frequency

in several stages, there will still be several harmonics at the output of the final multiplier stage. Only one of these harmonics is wanted: that at 1296MHz. The unwanted ones are removed by the three-stage filter at the end of the transmitter strip. When the unwanted sub-harmonics and harmonics are reduced to a very low level, that is, the output is on one frequency only, the output is said to be 'clean'. A transmitter must *never* be allowed to produce a 'dirty' signal which may be radiated on more than one frequency. A very important part of any microwave transmitter is good filtering so that the output is clean.

Use of frequency mixers

Fig 9.4 is the block diagram of a different type of transmitter. It uses the same sort of circuit to generate a crystal-controlled 'local oscillator' signal, this time *not* harmonically related to the final frequency. The local oscillator frequency is mixed with another 'intermediate frequency' (IF) to give the microwave frequency which is wanted. In the figure, a 96MHz crystal is used in the oscillator, and output is taken at three times this frequency (288MHz), doubled to 576MHz, then doubled again to 1152MHz. The block labelled 'mixer' takes this frequency and mixes it with the 144MHz IF to give two new frequencies which are 1152MHz + 144MHz = 1296MHz (wanted) and 1152MHz − 144MHz = 1008MHz (unwanted). The mixer output goes through a filter which removes most of the unwanted 1008MHz signal and

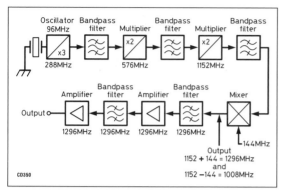

Fig 9.4. Block diagram of a mixer-type microwave transmitter

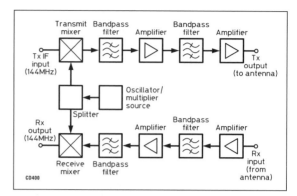

Fig 9.5. Block diagram of a microwave transverter

passes most of the wanted 1296MHz signal. The wanted signal is then amplified and filtered again until it is clean and powerful enough to be used as a transmitter.

You can, perhaps, now see that *exactly* the same oscillator and multiplier circuit, described earlier, can be used to supply the local oscillator signal in this type of transmitter. If the second signal is VFO controlled, say from an amateur 2m (144 to 146MHz) transceiver, then the microwave output frequency is variable too, according to the 2m frequency used. You should also be able to see that filters are just as important in this type of transmitter!

If you think a little more about it, you will see that exactly the same local oscillator frequency (1152MHz) can be used to mix with the received microwave frequency to produce a signal which can be tuned on the 2m receiver: 1296MHz − 1152MHz = 144MHz, 1297MHz − 1152MHz = 145MHz, and so on. Fig 9.5 shows the block diagram of a combined transmit and receive converter ('transverter') which uses one local oscillator source. This type of transmitter (and receiver combined together known as a 'transverter') will also be described here.

Special components and techniques

The design of suitable oscillator and multiplier stages is not too different to that used at lower frequencies, except that special microwave components sometimes need to be used and the circuit must also be built on a specially designed printed circuit board (PCB) to keep the circuit compact and efficient.

The special components which may be needed in the higher frequency stages can be very different. Many ordinary components are so big that they are a significant fraction of a wavelength in size, and so begin to act in strange ways as the frequency increases: they add 'stray' capacitance or inductance (or both) to the circuit. For instance, the body and leads of a resistor or capacitor might make the component appear like a tuned circuit. This is called 'self-resonance'. When there is self-resonance, a circuit that was designed as an amplifier might, instead, act as an oscillator – or even do nothing at all!

Unwanted 'stray' inductance (L) and capacitance (C) can only be avoided or reduced by using very low values and very short leads on ordinary miniature components or by using special components designed for use at microwave frequencies. These special components are usually 'leadless chips', that is, they do not have wire-end leads like the components used elsewhere and are also much smaller. The leads are replaced by metallised areas at each end of the component so that it can be soldered directly into the PCB without causing 'stray' effects. These small, leadless chip components are known as 'surface mount devices' (SMDs), as they are intended for mounting directly on the surface of the PCB.

Transistors and diodes have to be specially designed and often fit into holes in the PCB so that the flat (strip) leads can be made as short as possible when the device is soldered in place.

The small size of the special components, or the need for very short leads on the ordinary components, means that they can be quite easily damaged either by static electricity while handling them or by being overheated while being soldered into circuit. The next section will show you how to avoid this damage!

The other differences are that, at microwave frequencies, the PCB will almost always have a 'ground' (or earth) plane of unetched copper on the opposite side to the tracks, and the tuning 'coils' of tuned circuits are no longer used. They are replaced by lines printed on the circuit board. Input and output connections are made from printed conductors which act as matching circuits: this is known as 'microstrip' construction, and you will see some good examples of this in the designs which follow. Some of the designs use a mixture of ordinary components and special components, and ordinary construction and microstrip, depending on the frequency. The transmitter designs can cover any frequency within their bands, but the descriptions will assume that you want to work at the recommended frequencies, and such things as crystal frequencies will be given for these sub-bands.

Construction

How to avoid component damage

Most special microwave components are very small and easily damaged while building a design. Some components, for example Schottky diodes (mixers and detectors used in receivers or test equipment), microwave transistors and GaAsFETs (amplifiers and oscillators used in receivers and transmitters) can be damaged or destroyed by static electricity charges caused by handling, and some care must be taken to avoid the risk of damage.

Sensitive components come in sealed, foil-lined envelopes, in conductive plastic bags, conductive foam plastic or wrapped in metal foil. The first and most important thing is to leave the device in its wrapping until it is actually used. The second precaution is to ensure that the device is always the *last* component to be soldered in place in the circuit. Once in circuit the risk is less, since other components already in the circuit will usually provide a 'leakage' path to earth which will give protection against static.

Before handling the components, the constructor should know a little about sources of static. Walking across nylon or polyester (synthetic or man-made) carpets and wearing clothes made from the same materials are sources of static, especially when it is cold and dry. Static to several thousand volts can build up on your body (have you ever had an electric shock from a car-door handle when touched on a dry day?). Much lower 'earth leakage' voltages from a poorly earthed mains-voltage soldering iron are also a source of trouble and are often enough to cause damage.

Some precautions are given next: not all of them may be needed, but maybe better safe than sorry!

1. Don't walk across synthetic fibre carpets immediately before handling microwave devices.

2. Don't wear clothes of similar materials.

3. Use a low-voltage or gas-fired soldering iron. Ensure that the soldering iron is properly earthed while it is connected to its power supply. This is a commonsense safety precaution in any case.

4. It is a good idea to put a sheet of aluminium cooking foil on the bench and put everything (tools, components, equipment and so on) onto the foil. Work with your wrists resting on the foil, or frequently touch the foil while you are working. If you work in this way, many of the other precautions may not be needed.

5. Use a pair of crocodile clips and a flexible 'jumper' wire to connect the body of the soldering iron to the ground (earth) plane of the equipment while soldering components.

6. If the component leads allow it (the usual 'micro-x' type transistor will), place a small metal washer over the device before removing it from its packing, so that all leads are shorted together before and during handling. Alternatively it might be possible to use a small piece of aluminium foil (which will not solder) to do the same job, removing the foil once the device has been soldered in place.

7. A useful precaution which will avoid the risk of heat damage is to be sure that the surfaces to be soldered are very clean and tinned. Your soldering iron bit also needs to be clean and tinned. You can also use LMP (low melting point, silver loaded) solder which will help.

8. Immediately before handling the device, touch the earth of the equipment and the package protective foil to ensure that both are at the same potential.

9. Place the device in position, handling as little as possible.

10. Unplug the soldering iron from its power supply and quickly solder the device in place. You might need to reconnect the iron and do some of the soldering operations several times if the soldering iron cools off too quickly.

11. Finally, when connecting pieces of equipment together to form a complete operating system, for example, when installing mast-head equipment and remote transmit/receive switching, keep leads carrying supply voltages to the sensitive devices well away from other leads carrying RF or those leads which might carry voltage transients from relay switching. Supply and signal lines should be well screened and decoupled in any case, but keeping them apart can minimise pick-up, thus making decoupling easier.

Here are a few more things which may help you with successful construction:

- *Use only the recommended components.* Components salvaged from other equipment or the 'junk box' may not work too well. Surplus components, *especially semiconductors*, should not be used *unless recommended*, otherwise the design may not work as well as it should.

- You *must* use a good, screened box if you want stable, clean, reliable performance. Die-cast boxes, tinplate boxes or boxes made from offcuts of double-sided PCB material are all satisfactory, provided that you think about what you are trying to do.

- Keep ingoing supplies and ingoing/outgoing signals apart, screened and well decoupled where needed.

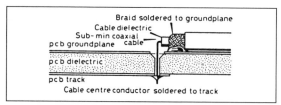

Fig 9.6. Right way of connecting coaxial cable directly to PCB

- Always use proper screened (coaxial) connections for signal frequencies. Figs 9.6 and 9.7 show some right and wrong ways to do this.
- Always build the design so that the shortest leads (or no leads at all) can be used. PCBs need to be 'stood off' their boxes using small metal pillars or nuts and bolts. Before mounting any components, place the bare PCB in its box and mark and drill mounting holes. Make sure that the board will fit the mountings *easily* before doing anything more. Drill any other holes needed.
- Use good-quality, thin (for example 22swg or finer) cored solder (60% tin, 40% lead), and be sure you can solder well and quickly. Even better, use silver-loaded solder. If in doubt, practise on a few scrap components and board until you can.

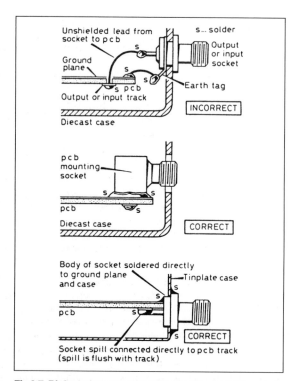

Fig 9.7. Right and wrong ways of connecting coaxial sockets to PCB

- Always solder inductors, resistors and capacitors first as these are less easily damaged by heat or static. Once these components are in place, the semiconductors can be more safely soldered into place.
- Be sure that transistors and other semiconductors (diodes and ICs) are the right way round: if they are not, they might become expensive, fast-acting fuses!
- You can align equipment without the need for expensive, professional test equipment if you think about what you are trying to do and then use simple instruments which you can build and own! These include directional couplers, detectors, absorption wavemeters and resistive loads etc. Some of these are described later.
- You might be able to use better test equipment, for either alignment or calibration, by asking another, more experienced amateur to help or guide you. It's not a bad idea to know which amateurs near you could help in any case!
- Finally, microwave transmitter (or receiver and antenna) construction and operation is *not* as easy for the Novice as getting onto the lower-frequency bands where almost 'anything goes'! You *must* want to learn about new ways of construction, new components and new ways of operating if you decide to use the microwave bands. One thing is certain, you will learn many new things if you decide you want to use the Novice microwave amateur bands. We hope you will enjoy using the wide-open freedom of the amateur microwave bands. *Don't be afraid to ask other amateurs for help!*

A high-quality oscillator source for the 1.3GHz band (G4DDK-001)

This oscillator/multiplier source was originally designed by Sam Jewell, G4DDK, to provide two 10mW outputs at 1152MHz for use in a 1296MHz transverter with an intermediate frequency (IF) of 144MHz. You can use it on its own as a low-power transmitter with a suitable crystal anywhere in the range 1000 to 1350MHz. It can have a single output of 20mW if you use it as a transmitter or two 10mW outputs if you use it as the local oscillator in a transverter (receive and transmit converter).

Although the track side of the board is shown to exact size in Fig 9.8, you shouldn't to try to make your own board. The material of the board and the accuracy of etching are both critical and home-made boards may not work as well as the properly produced PCBs which are available from the RSGB Microwave Committee Component Service (see later). These PCBs (G4DDK-001) are ready drilled, slotted and tinned, completely ready for building. Some of the possible uses of the board are shown as block diagrams in Fig 9.9.

Circuit description

The circuit of the oscillator source is given in Fig 9.10 and the component values in Table 9.1.

The crystal oscillator uses a circuit known as the 'Butler oscillator'. This oscillator consists of two stages: a high-gain amplifier (TR1) and a separate limiter (TR2). The output of TR1 is tuned to the crystal overtone frequency by a highly damped (broad or 'low-Q') tuned circuit consisting of L1, C3 and R4. Output is taken to the limiter stage input via C2. Feedback to the emitter of TR1 is via the crystal X1 which is of very high Q. The phase of the feedback controls oscillation at the crystal overtone frequency. Because of the limiting action of TR2 the output at its collector has many harmonics. A tuned circuit consisting of L2 and C7 tunes the wanted harmonic. This can be any harmonic, from the oscillator overtone frequency to

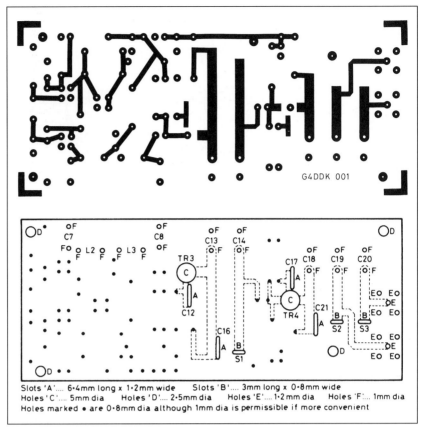

Slots 'A'.... 6·4mm long x 1·2mm wide   Slots 'B'.... 3mm long x 0·8mm wide
Holes 'C'.... 5mm dia   Holes 'D'.... 2·5mm dia   Holes 'E'.... 1·2mm dia   Holes 'F'.... 1mm dia
Holes marked ● are 0·8mm dia although 1mm dia is permissible if more convenient

Fig 9.8. Printed circuit track layout (top) and drilling details (bottom) for the microwave source G4DDK-001, shown full size

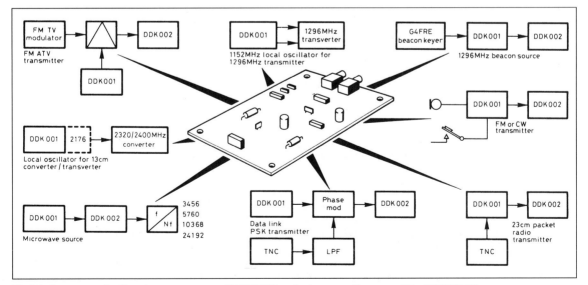

Fig 9.9. Some uses for the microwave source G4DDK-001 and microwave linear amplifier G4DDK-002

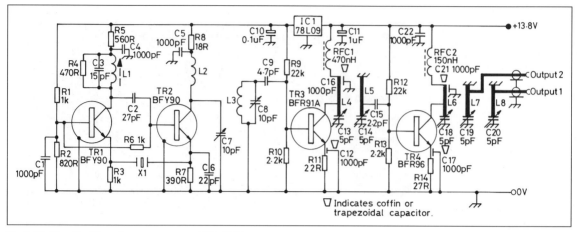

Fig 9.10. Circuit of the microwave source G4DDK-001

about the fifth harmonic, but the output level of the higher harmonics will be less than the lower harmonics. This simply means that you shouldn't try to use the circuit beyond the fourth or fifth harmonic, otherwise the next multiplier will not work properly.

The oscillator operates with a crystal overtone frequency between 90 and 110MHz, although by changing the value of C3 the circuit can be made to operate reliably between about 84 and 120MHz. For operation in the various recommended parts of the band, the overtone crystal frequency should be chosen using the simple calculation given in Table 9.1. A 9V integrated circuit regulator (78L09) stabilises the supply to the oscillator and limiter stages. The third stage is a doubler (×2 multiplier). Input, in the frequency range 250 to 330MHz, is taken by C9 from the high-impedance end of the tuned

Table 9.1. Components list for the 1.3GHz oscillator/multiplier/low-power transmitter, G4DDK-001

RESISTORS

R1, 3, 6	1k
R2	820R
R4	470R
R5	560R
R7	390R
R8	18R
R9, 12	22k
R10, 13	2k2
R11	22R
R14	27R

Resistors are 0.25W miniature carbon film or metal film.

CAPACITORS

C1, 4, 5, 22	1000p high-K ceramic plate, eg Philips 629 series
C12, 16, 17, 21	1n trapezoidal capacitor from RSGB Microwave Component Service or Piper
C10	0.1µ tantalum bead, 16V working
C11	1µ tantalum bead, 16V working
C3	15p low-K ceramic plate, eg Philips 632 series
C7, 8	5mm trimmer, 10p maximum
C13, 14	5mm trimmer, 5p maximum
C18–20	5mm trimmer, 5p maximum. Must be able to reach 0.9pF minimum, eg Sky (green) or Murata TZ03 (black)
C23	1000p screw-in feedthrough capacitor

INDUCTORS

L1	Toko S18 5.5 turn (green) with aluminium core

L2, 3	3 turns of 22swg tinned or enamelled copper wire. Inside diameter 3mm. Turns spaced 1 wire diameter, height of coil 5mm above board
L4–8	Printed on the PCB
RFC1	470n axial-lead type
RFC2	150n axial-lead type
RFC3	2 turns of lead-in wire through two-hole ferrite bead (not critical)

SEMICONDUCTORS

TR1, 2	BFY90 available from Cirkit, Bonex, Piper etc
TR3	BFR91A available from Cirkit, Bonex, Piper etc
TR4	BFR96 available from Cirkit, Bonex, Piper etc
IC1	78L08 from Piper, STC Components etc
D1	Any small silicon diode, eg 1N418, 1N419 (reverse supply protection)

MISCELLANEOUS

X1	Fifth overtone crystal in HC18/U case (frequency of crystal = F_{out}/12)

PCB, 1152MHz LO PCB G4DDK-001, RSGB Microwave Committee Components Service
Thin copper strip for grounding the tuned lines where shown. This can be obtained from many model shops
Die-cast box, 127 × 78 × 45mm, Eddystone Radio 27134 or 114 × 64 × 30mm RS Components 509-939
Sub-miniature coaxial socket(s), SMB or SMC PCB-mounting type recommended. BNC could be used (see text)
Four M2.5 bolts about 15mm long
About 17 M2.5 nuts
Crystal heater (optional), Murata "Posistor" type PTH507B01BM500N016

circuit formed by L3 and C8. The output of TR3 is tuned by the coupled microstrip band-pass circuits L4/C13 and L5/C14 to the range 500 to 660MHz.

A high-impedance tap on L5 couples the doubled signal to the base of the final multiplier stage, TR4. The output of this stage is tuned and filtered by three coupled, tuned microstrip lines: L6/C18, L7/C19 and L8/C20. The tuning range of this filter is highly dependent upon the type of trimmer capacitors chosen for C18, 19 and 20. Using the specified capacitors, the filter will tune from 980 to 1400MHz, covering the range of second harmonics from the previous stage (1000 to 1320MHz).

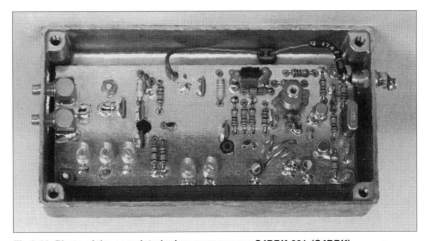

Fig 9.11. Photo of the completed microwave source G4DDK-001 *(G4DDK)*

Three stages of filtering are used to give very clean output at output 1. A slightly less clean output is available at output 2, since this is taken from the second stage of the filter. Even so, the output here is fine for use in a receive converter with output 1 being used for the transmit converter. Each output is at a level of about 10mW.

Only one output is required for a low-powered transmitter. This is taken from output 1. If you think you will never want two outputs, you can cut the track to output 2 where it leaves L7 – if you do this you will have one output of about 20mW at output 1. If you think you might at some time want two outputs, then instead of cutting the track, you could fit a 1mm circuit pin into the output 2 pad and solder a 50Ω chip resistor between the pin and the ground plane on the *upper* side of the board. This will terminate output 2 correctly, leaving a single output of 10mW at output 1. If the PCB is used later for a transverter, the pin and resistor can easily be removed and the two 10mW outputs will still be available for the transverter. If you align the PCB as described later and you use either modification, the transmitter output at output 1 is clean enough to be connected to an antenna without further filtering.

Construction

Fig 9.11 is a photograph of a finished unit and Fig 9.12 shows the layout of the components on the ground-plane side of the board, together with some of the component lead connections.

1. Construction should start with fitting the bare board into its box (see earlier), marking the centres of the mounting holes and drilling them (M2.5). All the other 'mechanical' things should follow, once the board is

mounted: it should be easily mounted in, or removed from, the box. Exact drilling measurements are not given because the constructor might choose to make his/her own box from pieces of unetched PCB material, copper, brass or tinplate, rather than use the recommended die-cast box, although the die-cast box is a much better way for a beginner to build the equipment. Whatever enclosure is used, the track side of the board should stand at least 5mm off the bottom of the box, using small metal pillars or nuts on 10mm × M2.5 bolts fitted through holes in the bottom of the box. The board is held in place by nuts fitted above the top of the board.

2. Once you are satisfied that the board will fit easily, then you can drill the other holes needed for the power connections (positive via the screw-in feedthrough capacitor, negative connected to a solder-tag bolted to the box wall) and output socket(s). Only when these jobs are done can you start to solder the components to the board!

3. First, cut the copper grounding strips and solder them into the slots at positions S1, 2 and 3.

4. The trapezoidal capacitors are next carefully soldered into the slots in the board where shown in the component overlay diagram. The correct way to solder them is shown in Fig 9.13. Make sure that the grounded side of trimmer capacitors C7, 8, 13, 14, 18, 19 and 20 are all soldered to both the top and bottom of the board. Capacitors C18, 19 and 20 should be miniature 5mm diameter foil types such as Sky or Murata. You must *not* use larger (7mm) trimmers, such as the popular Dau or Philips types, as these lead to tuning problems. The circuit was designed to take the small types. This also applies to C7, 8, 13 and 14.

5. Wind the coils L2 and L3 as shown and solder them

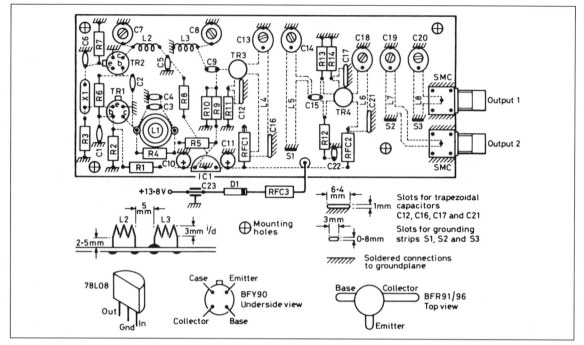

Fig 9.12. Component layout and some component details for the microwave source G4DDK-001

carefully at the height shown above the PCB ground plane.

6. Small PCB connectors such as type SMA, SMB or SMC (CONHEX) are soldered to the output(s) where shown. You need only one connector if you are only using output 1, but two if you intend to use both outputs. When you fit the board into the die-cast box, the connector(s) will need to protrude through a hole in the end wall of the box. Alternatively, a short length of small-diameter coaxial cable (eg RG174) can be soldered directly to the board (see Fig 9.6 for the right way to do it!) and taken to a BNC socket mounted on the end of the box. Do *not* try to use SO239 so-called 'UHF' connectors – they are too big and simply don't work properly at these frequencies!

Alignment

It is assumed that you are starting with a crystal frequency of about 108MHz to produce a single output at about 1296MHz. It is easier to test and align the board out of its box, which is why you should be sure that the board

fits easily onto its mountings in the box! You will need the following test equipment:

- 50Ω terminated power meter
- Analogue (moving-coil) multimeter
- Absorption wavemeter(s) covering 80 to 1300MHz

The reason you shouldn't use a digital multimeter is that digital meters do not work in 'real time' and they show changes *after* they have been made, rather than *as* they are made!

1. Connect your multimeter, set to the 500mA range, in series with the positive supply lead to the unit.
2. Connect DC power (+12 to 13.5V) and check the current drawn is no more than about 150mA. If it is much more, then check for short-circuits or wrongly placed components.
3. When all is well, start alignment. Place an absorption wavemeter pick-up coil close to L1 and tune to 108MHz. You should see a strong reading on the meter.
4. Peak the reading by turning the core of L1.
5. Turn the power on and off to check that the oscillator re-starts properly. If it doesn't, then turn the core of L1 about a quarter turn and try again. Don't worry about the exact frequency yet; an error of a few kilohertz doesn't matter at this stage and you won't be able to measure it so closely with the absorption wavemeter anyway!

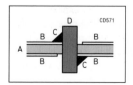

Fig 9.13. Soldering the trapezoidal capacitors to the PCB. A: epoxy glass board; B: PCB track; C: solder fillet; D: trapezoidal capacitor

6. Set a *moving-coil* (important!) multimeter to the 2.5V range (or nearest equivalent) and measure the voltage between the top end of R11 and earth. This should be no more than a few hundred millivolts.

7. Peak the reading by slowly tuning C7 and C8.

8. Check the frequency tuned is 324MHz by placing the coil of the wavemeter close to L3.

9. Transfer the meter leads across R14, and peak the reading by slowly tuning C13 and C14.

10. Again check the correct harmonic (648MHz) has been tuned by using the wavemeter.

11. Connect a low-power wattmeter (see later) to the output and slowly tune C18, 19 and 20 for a maximum reading.

12. Check that the correct harmonic (1296MHz) has been tuned by using the wavemeter.

13. You should now go back and *slightly* re-peak the trimmers for an absolute maximum reading at the 1296MHz output.

Final setting of the frequency of the crystal oscillator can be done once the completed, aligned board is in its box, either by using an accurate frequency counter or by listening for the source on a calibrated receiver. You will probably need to find another amateur locally who has either of these two things to help you. You can then adjust L1 to bring the signal onto the correct receiver dial calibration, although this is not too important when the board is used as a transmitter and not as part of a transverter.

If you can't pull the frequency to *exactly* 12 times that marked on the crystal, then it is very likely you have a non-standard crystal. Pulling the frequency too far can make the oscillator fail to re-start after switching off and then on. The cure is to put a small-value ceramic plate capacitor, say 10 to 33pF, in series with the crystal by cutting the PCB track near to the crystal and bridging the gap (on the underside of the board) with the capacitor. If you have to do this modification, then you *must* keep the leads of the new capacitor short and use a capacitor with a zero temperature coefficient, otherwise the frequency may drift too much as the crystal oscillator warms up. To get the best stability, you could fit a miniature crystal heater to keep the crystal at a constant temperature. This simply clips over the crystal case and is connected to the +12V supply. The earth connection to the crystal heater is made through the crystal case – make sure this is soldered to ground!

Simple modulator for speech and FSK/AFSK

You can frequency modulate, or frequency-shift key, the transmitter by using the simple circuit shown in Fig 9.14. This modulator circuit is only suitable for NBFM (speech frequencies). If you try to use it for wide-band modulation, for example for high-speed data/packet, it will

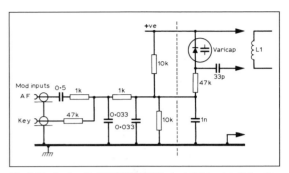

Fig 9.14. A simple FM/FSK/AFSK modulator circuit for the microwave source G4DDK-001. Components to the right of the dotted line must be wired with very short, rigid leads directly onto the track side of the PCB close to L1

produce a mixture of frequency and phase modulation which can't be decoded properly.

The modulator circuit should be built on the underside of the board with the components to the right of the dotted line connected with very short, rigid leads across L1. Note that C3 should be changed to 33pF if the modulator is fitted. The external connections for microphone and key *must* be via feedthrough capacitors to stop hum and noise being picked up and modulating the oscillator.

If you are going to use the source as a personal beacon, it should be identified by frequency-shift keying with an 800Hz frequency shift. This can be used with the same circuit, although the 'sense' of the deviation should be such that the 'mark' signal (carrier only) is at the beacon frequency and 'space' keys the beacon low in frequency by 800Hz, returning to mark for each dot or dash. With the circuit given, this means the keying voltage should be low for 'mark' and high for 'space': that is, 'mark' is generated with an earth on the keying lead.

A 1W linear amplifier for 1152MHz to 1300MHz (G4DDK-002)

This amplifier was also designed by Sam Jewell, G4DDK, and provides 1W output at 1152MHz when driven by 10mW from the G4DDK-001 oscillator board. It was originally intended for driving frequency multipliers to the higher amateur microwave bands.

The board can be used at frequencies as high as 1300MHz. It can also be used with the 1296MHz version of the oscillator board, just described, to make a 1W transmitter.

The amplifier is linear so it will amplify *any* modulation mode and will provide drive suitable, later on, for a Mitsubishi M57762 PA 'block' which requires just 1W drive for more than 10W output across the whole of the 1.3GHz band. The half-power (3dB) bandwidth of the prototype 1W amplifier was 58MHz, suggesting it could also be suitable for 24cm ATV operation.

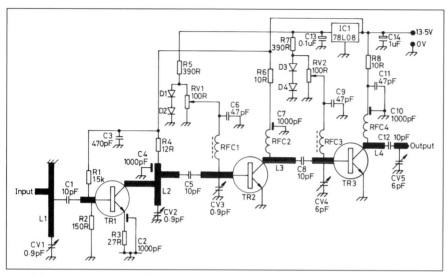

Fig 9.15. Circuit of the 1W microwave linear amplifier G4DDK-002

The first stage operates in Class A, at a quiescent (no drive) collector current of 17mA. The second stage operates in Class AB, also at a quiescent current of 17mA. A BFQ34 is used in the output stage. Maximum output at 1152MHz may be as much as 1.5W with a selected device. Class AB operation at a quiescent current of 35mA is used. A Motorola MRF511 can be used as a replacement for the often-difficult-to-get BFQ34. If this transistor is used, you will need to add a 5 to 10pF trimmer between TR3 collector and ground if you are to get full gain from the transistor.

If only 300 to 400mW output is needed, it is possible to leave out the BFQ34 and its bias components. In this case, take the output from the base 'pad' vacated by TR3. The match to 50Ω at this point is excellent.

Construction

The track layout is shown full size in Fig 9.16, the layout in Fig 9.17 and component values in Table 9.2. A PCB is available from the RSGB Microwave Committee Component Service and you are recommended to use this, rather than trying to make a suitable board. Again, the board is fully drilled, slotted and tinned, ready for construction. The board is best mounted in a die-cast box.

The top copper surface of the board is used as a ground plane and the matching lines and component connections etched on the track side.

1. Use a small file to form the sides of TR2 and TR3 mounting holes to take copper foil strips, used to obtain low-inductance grounding of the emitters.

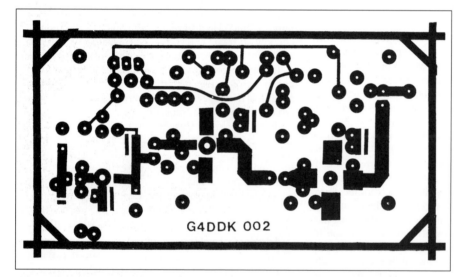

Fig 9.16. Printed circuit track layout for the 1W amplifier G4DDK-002, shown full size

Circuit description

The circuit of the amplifier is shown in Fig 9.15. It will provide 20dB gain (10mW in for 1W out) with just two stages, but it is better to keep the gain in each stage lower as this usually means better stability and less dependence on selected devices. The first stage of the amplifier uses a BFR91A bipolar transistor, although slightly better results were obtained in the prototype with an NEC NE021, since compression in the first stage tends to limit the final output to 1W. Operating the amplifier at much more than 1W output increases dissipation in the output stage and makes the BFQ34 more likely to fail in use.

2. As before, place the PCB into the box where it is to be housed and mark the position of the M2.5 mounting holes and TR3 stud on the base of the box.

3. Drill the holes and make sure the PCB fits easily before you start to solder any components to it. The positions of the components on the PCB are shown in Fig 9.17.

4. Solder a strip of copper foil through the L1 grounding slot.

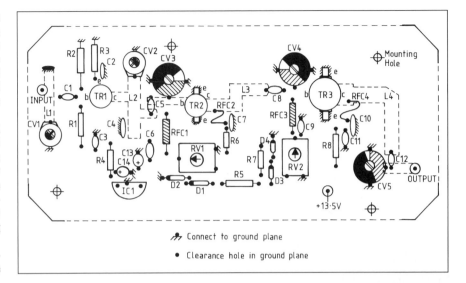

5. Solder two slightly wider strips in the filed flats for TR2 and TR3 emitter grounds.

6. Solder all components except the transistors into place, taking care to solder the ground leads on both top and bottom of the board. Check the polarity of the tantalum capacitors before soldering. Take care not to overheat the trapezoidal capacitors.

7. As before, the transistors, diodes and the IC are soldered last. Check all three transistors are the right way round before soldering them in place. Also check the polarity of the diodes and IC1 before soldering. The BFQ34 should be soldered so that the transistor leads are flat to the tracks on the board. The top cap of the transistor fits through the hole in the board with its top level with the ground plane of the board.

8. Solder suitable short lengths of miniature coaxial cable to the input and output. The prototype used RG174 terminated with SMC plugs. The correct way of using the miniature cable is shown in Fig 9.6.

9. Even for alignment, a small heatsink will be required on the stud of TR3. This can be a small block or sheet of aluminium drilled to take the stud of the transistor. It should be held in place by means of nuts screwed onto the stud.

Alignment

It is easier to test and align the board out of its box. For alignment the following test equipment is required:

- 50Ω power meter load
- Analogue multimeter
- Wavemeter(s) to cover 80MHz to 1.5GHz

1. Set the trimmer capacitors to the initial positions shown.

Fig 9.17. Top: component layout for the 1W amplifier G4DDK-002, ground-plane side. Bottom: photograph of completed unit in die-cast box *(G3PFR)*

2. Set the bias resistors RV1 and RV2 so that the rotors are at the ground end, which will give no bias voltage on TR2 and TR3.

3. Before connecting any power, check and then recheck that all components are in the right place and that those components that should have ground connections are actually soldered to ground on both top and bottom of the board.

4. Connect the amplifier output to a 50Ω power meter/load. *Do not* connect any drive to the amplifier.

5. Connect a 13.5V supply to the amplifier and check across R3 for a reading of 0.44V; this corresponds to a current of 17mA. If wrong, recheck the circuit, looking especially for short-circuits or incorrectly placed components.

Table 9.2. Components list for the 1W amplifier G4DDK-002

RESISTORS

R1	1k5
R2	150R
R3	27R
R4	12R
R5, 7	390R
R6, 8	10R
RV1, 2	100R 0.25W carbon track potentiometer, horizontal mounting

Resistors are 0.25W miniature carbon film or metal film.

CAPACITORS

C1, 5, 8, 12	10p miniature ceramic plate or disc capacitor
C2, 4, 7 10	470 to 1n trapezoidal (coffin) capacitor
C6, 9	47p miniature ceramic plate or disc capacitor
C13	0.1µ tantalum bead, 10V working minimum
C14	1µ tantalum bead, 16V working minimum
CV1, 2	0.9p minimum foil trimmer, Sky, Oxley or Murata
CV3, 4, 5	Mullard 808 series 6p foil trimmer

SEMICONDUCTORS

TR1	BFR91A, NE021
TR2	BFG34
TR3	BFQ34
D1–4	1N914, 1N4148
IC1	78L08

INDUCTORS

RFC1, 3	1µH miniature moulded choke
RFC2, 4	1.5 turns of 1mm diameter tinned copper wire, 3mm inside diameter, self-supporting
L1–4	Printed lines on 1/16in double-sided glass epoxy board

MISCELLANEOUS

PCB for 1152MHz amp: PCB G4DDK-002, RSGB Microwave Committee Component Service

Thin copper strip for grounding where shown. This can be obtained from many model shops

Die-cast box, 127 × 78 × 45mm, Eddystone Radio 27134 or 114 × 64 × 30mm RS Components 509-939

Sub-miniature coaxial socket(s), SMA, SMB or SMC types recommended. BNC could be used (see text)

Four M2.5 bolts, about 15mm long

About 17 M2.5 nuts

---

6. When all is well, go on to check for 8V at the output of IC1.

7. Check for approximately 1.4V at the junction of R5 and D1 and also the junction of R7 and D3.

8. Place the voltmeter leads across R6 and adjust RV1 for a reading of 0.17V (17mA). Three hands are preferred for this operation! The rotor of RV1 will be set around half-way for normal operation.

9. Place the voltmeter leads across R8 and adjust RV2 for a reading of 0.35V (35mA quiescent current). Make these adjustments *carefully and slowly* to avoid excessive bias and possible destruction of the transistors.

10. The oscillator (drive) input can now be connected: no more than 10mW is needed.

11. With the specified trimmers, set initially as shown, it should be only be necessary to slightly readjust CV1 and CV2 for a reading on the output meter. Also slightly readjust CV3, CV4 and CV5 for maximum output. You may need to go back and readjust all trimmers several times for maximum output.

12. Loosely couple the wavemeter to the amplifier output. A directional coupler is useful for this purpose. Tune the wavemeter over its entire range, checking for unwanted responses that may indicate spurious oscillation in the amplifier.

13. Disconnect the input drive and check that the amplifier output falls to zero as shown by no reading on the power meter. The amplifier should be unconditionally stable, showing no sign of oscillation at any setting of the various trimmers. Of course there may always be exceptions! The amplifier is now ready to be boxed and used.

Finishing off

The amplifier is best housed in a suitable die-cast box (see Table 9.2). The diagonal cutouts on the corners of the PCB are there to allow you to fit the board comfortably into its box.

Four M2.5 screws are passed through the base of the box and the board stood off from the inside of the box using two M2.5 nuts as spacers on each screw. Don't forget the hole for the TR3 stud to pass through the box! Careful use of spacer washers will be needed to ensure the capstan (body) of TR3 is correctly spaced from the base of the box. The best way to do this is to carefully measure the required spacing and then cut and file a suitable-size aluminium block as the spacer. If large enough, it will be a better heatsink than the base of the die-cast box. It will help to put a *little* heatsink grease on the stud, the heatsink block and the bottom of the die-cast box where the block is in contact with it.

The box will need drilling for two sockets (or miniature cables), one for the input and one for the output. You should use a bolt-in feedthrough capacitor of 1 to 10nF to carry the DC supply into the box. The negative of the supply should be grounded using a solder tag bolted to the side of the box.

A mixer-type transmitter (and receiver)

Another good way of building a transmitter (and receiver at the same time) is to use mixers from a common amateur intermediate frequency (IF), in this case 144 to 146MHz. If a local oscillator source at exactly 1152MHz is used, then the transmitter output will be 144MHz + 1152MHz = 1296MHz and 145MHz + 1152MHz = 1297MHz, and so on. On receive, 1296MHz – 1152MHz = 144MHz and 1297MHz – 1152MHz = 145MHz and so on. The local oscillator source at 1152MHz can be the G4DDK source just described, crystalled at 96.0000MHz.

The transmitter (and receiver) design is a circuit and layout by Rick Campbell, KK7B, which was described in the 1992 *ARRL Handbook*. A single PCB uses printed 'hairpin' filters, diode ring-mixers and silicon microwave monolithic integrated circuit (MMIC) amplifiers. It gives linear, known and stable 50Ω, 'no-tune', gain on both transmit and receive in the 1296 to 1298MHz narrow-band part of the band using an 1152MHz local oscillator (LO), although the bandwidth is such that the whole of the band from 1240 to 1325MHz can be covered by using a different LO frequency and the same 144 to 146MHz IF.

The transmitter (and receiver) is built on a single 5 by 7in (127 × 178mm) glassfibre/epoxy PCB which is available from several sources (see Appendix 2). Although an LO diode multiplier is included in the original design, this stage is not used if the LO source used is the G4DDK-001 already described: the multiplier is replaced by a re-sistive attenuator to adjust the level of LO injection down from the +13dBm (20mW) available from the G4DDK-001 board.

The circuit is shown as a block diagram in Fig 9.18

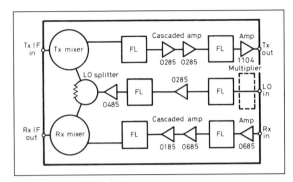

Fig 9.18. Block diagram of the KK7B 144MHz to 1.3GHz 'no-tune' transverter *(ARRL Handbook)*

and as a full schematic in Fig 9.19(a), the modifications using the G4DDK-001 oscillator source in Fig 9.19(b), while the component layout is given in Fig 9.20(a) and 9.20(b), and the values in Table 9.3.

Construction

1. Carefully drill four 2.5 or 3mm mounting holes in the board, preferably where shown in Fig 9.20, al-though this is not critical.

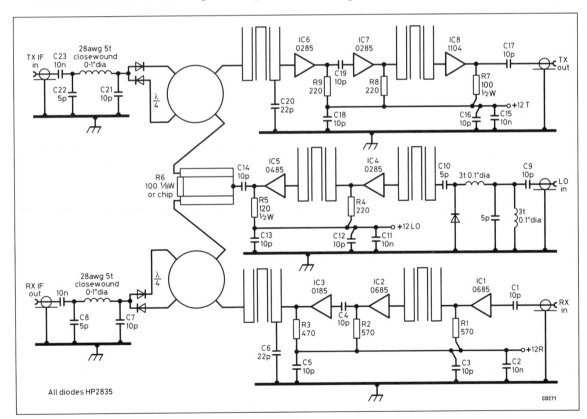

Fig 9.19(a). Circuit of the KK7B transverter *(ARRL Handbook)*

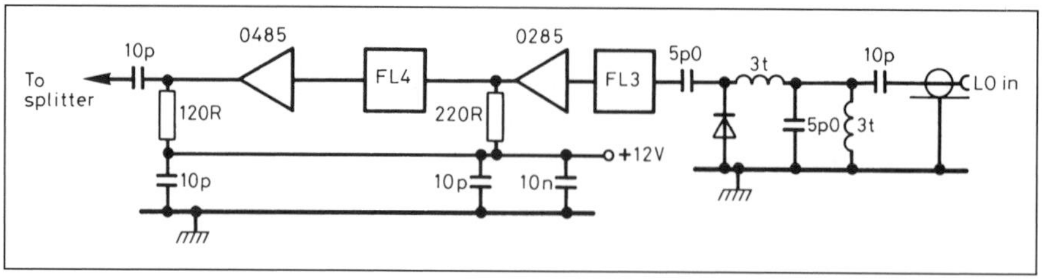

2. Using the board as a template, mark the mounting hole centres into the box or case you are going to use to house the transverter board, LO drive source and any other associated circuits (see later for suggestions).

Fig 9.19(b). Original transverter circuit

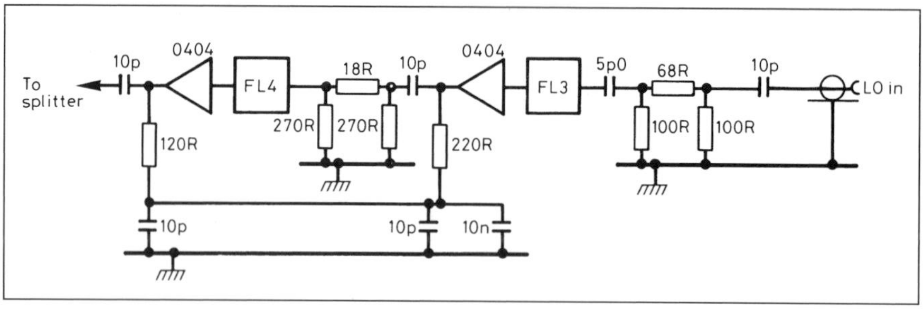

3. Drill the holes and make sure that the board will fit easily onto the bolts used to fix the board in place, just as for the other circuits described earlier. A suitable box has not been specified as the type and size of the box will depend on what else you want to put into the box beside the transverter board.

Fig 9.19(c). Modified transverter circuit

4. Drill clearance holes for the MMICs where shown in Fig 9.20: 2.2 to 2.5mm for the xx85 packages and 3.8 to 4mm for the xx04 packages. These holes will allow the packages to lie flush to the board with minimum lead length, just like the transistors in the circuits described earlier.

5. Drill 1mm holes for the grounding pins where shown in Fig 9.20.

6. Fit the pins with their heads on the track side of the PCB, pushing the heads down flush to the surface of the board.

7. Solder the pins on *both sides* of the board. Cut off any excess length on the ground-plane side of the board after soldering.

8. When this work is finished, you can mount the inductors, capacitors and input/output sockets. The bodies of the sockets are soldered directly to the edge of the board (top and bottom) and the spills directly to the tracks.

9. Finally, solder in the MMICs (make sure you get them the right way round!) and the bias (supply) resistors. All the small 'chip' (SMD) components are best soldered with a very small soldering iron and silver-loaded LMP (low melting point) solder, as they can easily be overheated and damaged if you are not good at soldering!

Note that the MMIC ends of the bias resistors are left deliberately long, as shown in Fig 9.20, so that the leads form inductances which improve the stability

and high-frequency performance of the MMICs. Before soldering R7 in place, slip a ferrite bead onto the MMIC end of the resistor lead, close to the solder pad: this increases the lead inductance still further and ensures the stability and gain of IC8, the transmitter output stage.

10. Once all the components are in place, check that they are all in the right places and, for the MMICs and diodes, they are connected the right way round! Check also that there are no obvious short-circuits – some of the components are very small and the gaps in the tracks even smaller. Look particularly for solder 'bridges' and remove them if there are any.

To use the transverter properly for both transmit and receive, you will need to arrange for low-loss (coaxial) switching at both the IF (144 to 146MHz) and the microwave frequency, together with power supply switching between the transmitter and the receiver. The LO, of course, runs all the time.

It is, however, possible to check and use the transmitter without this switching, as follows.

1. Connect a 50Ω load/detector (see later) to the transmitter output socket, a +12V supply to the points marked '+12V T' and '+12V LO' but *not* to the point marked '+12V R'.

2. Connect the G4DDK-001 output to the 'LO' socket and a 1mW signal source at 144MHz to the socket marked 'TX IF'.

3. Connect a meter on its 500mA scale in series with the +12V supply lead to the transverter board.

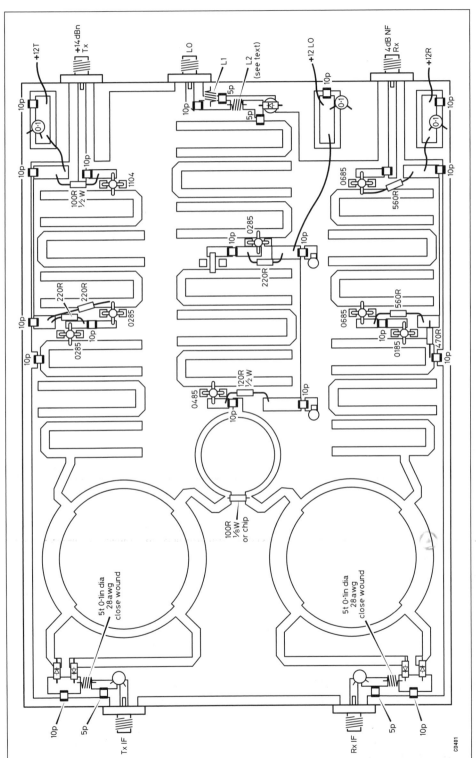

Fig 9.20(a). Component layout for the KK7B transverter *(ARRL Handbook)*. Where earthed connections are shown, the board must be drilled to take 1mm circuit pins to provide through-board grounding. Similarly, it may be necessary to drill mounting holes and clearance holes for the MMIC bodies (see text). Some voltage supply resistor leads are shown as long leads; this is quite deliberate as it provides the necessary lead inductance which helps to decouple the MMIC

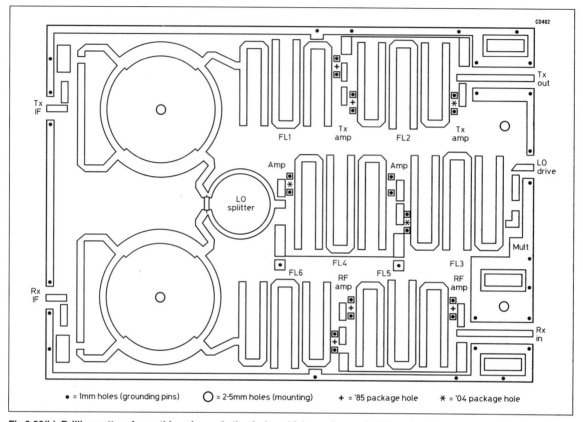

Fig 9.20(b). Drilling pattern for earthing pins and other holes which may be needed. Note that the location of none of the holes is critical

4. Switch on the +12V supply: the current taken should be about 200 to 220mA.

5. Switch on the LO source and the 1mW 144MHz drive source: if all is well, you should see about 20mW output indicated on the load/detector. If either the LO or the 144MHz source is switched off, this output should disappear, showing that the transmitter is stable. (*Important*: the drive level must not be greater than about 2mW, otherwise the mixer diodes may be damaged and the transmit MMICs may be overdriven,

become non-linear and cause unwanted outputs such as harmonics to be generated).

Suitable coaxial switches are available from one of the suppliers listed in Appendix 2. If you want to use the KK7B transverter properly, then this kind of control and interface is a 'must'.

A transverter control circuit, designed by G3SEK, was described in Chapter 18 (Volume 3) of the RSGB *Microwave Handbook*: it is very suitable for controlling this transverter from a low-powered (3W) 144MHz transceiver. A suitable alternative is a control and interface design by G4JNT, a PCB for which is available from the RSGB Microwave Committee Components Service.

Test equipment and test methods for the 1.3GHz band

The sort of measurements you will need to make while aligning your microwave transmitters are either amplitude/power measurements or frequency measurements.

Fig 9.20(c). Layout of the additional components (attenuators) to allow use of the G4DDK-001 local oscillator

Table 9.3. Component table for the KK7B 144/1296MHz transverter

RESISTORS

R1, 2	570R, 0.25W carbon film or metal film
R3	470R, 0.25W carbon film or metal film
R4, 5	150R, 0.5W carbon film or metal film
R6	100R, 0.125W carbon film, metal film or 1205 size SMD
R7	100R, 0.5W carbon film or metal film
R8, 9	220R, 0.25W carbon film or metal film
R10, 12	100R, 0.125W, 1206 size SMD
R11	68R, 0.125W, 1206 size SMD
R13, 15	270R, 0.125W, 1206 size SMD
R14	18R, 0.125W, 1206 size SMD

NOTE: resistor values calculated for 12V power rail, to give correct supply voltages (V_{cc}) at MMIC collectors with manufacturer's recommended standing current. R4, R5 and R7 *must* be 0.5W rating.

CAPACITORS

C1, 3, 4, 5, 7, 9, 12, 13, 14, 16, 17, 18, 21	10p high-stability COG/NP0 1206 size SMD
C6, 20	22p high-stability COG/NP0 1206 size SMD
C8, 10, 22	5p high-stability COG/NP0 1206 size SMD
C2, 11, 15, 23, 24	0.01µ (100n) sub-miniature discs or X7R 1206 size SMD

All capacitors are 50V working.

SEMICONDUCTORS

IC1, 2	Avantek MSA0685 MMIC or similar
IC3	Avantek MSA0185 MMIC or similar
IC4, 5	Avantek MSA0404 MMIC or similar
IC6, 7	Avantek MSA0285 MMIC or similar
IC8	Avantek MSA1104 MMIC or similar
D1–4	Hewlett-Packard HP2835 Schottky mixer diodes or Philips BA481 Schottky mixer diodes

MISCELLANEOUS

Printed circuit board (see Appendix 2)
Five miniature 50Ω coaxial sockets, SMA, SMB, SMC or BNC (NOT SO239!)
Approx 40 1mm circuit pins (for grounding, see text)
Approx 2ft 30swg (28awg) enamelled copper wire
LO source: G4DDK-001, crystal = 96.0000MHz for LO at 1152MHz
Input (signal) attenuator (see text). Signal drive required is approximately 1mW (any mode), in range 144 to 146MHz for output at 1296 to 1298MHz
Two 50Ω coaxial relays for input/output switching (see text)

Power measurements at 1.3GHz will usually be in the range of a few milliwatts up to possibly 5W.

In a 1.3GHz transmitter, you will need to measure the starting (crystal) frequency, sub-harmonic frequencies, transmitter output frequency and harmonics. It doesn't matter whether the transmitter is a simple oscillator/multiplier type or a more complicated mixer transmitter: you will still need to make similar measurements during alignment and to ensure that the output is clean. This means that you will need to have a wavemeter (or more than one wavemeter) which will allow you to measure

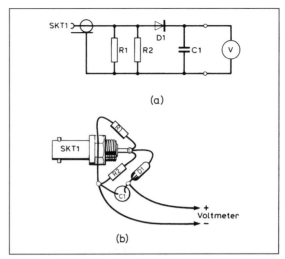

Fig 9.21. Circuit and layout for a simple VHF/UHF milliwatt power meter. This layout will not work at microwave frequencies, although the basic circuit will

frequencies between about 80MHz and 2.6GHz, higher if possible.

Power measurement and detection at 1.3GHz

Fig 9.21 shows the circuit and layout of the simplest VHF/UHF milliwatt power meter. This circuit and layout works well to about 400 or perhaps 500MHz, after which stray inductances and capacitances arising from the lead length or the size of the components limit its usefulness. The meter measures the peak RF voltage across the load (R1 and R2), minus the forward voltage drop across the detector diode. Divided by √2 (1.414), this gives the RMS (root mean square) value from which the power can be calculated using the equation:

$$P = \frac{V \times V}{2 \times R}$$

where V is the peak voltage (RMS volts × 1.414), P is the power in watts and R is the load resistance (50Ω here).

For germanium diodes (eg OA47 or similar), where the circuit impedance is 50Ω, the relationship will be:

$$P = \frac{(V + 0.25) \times (V + 0.25)}{2 \times 50}$$

(Forward voltage drop = 0.25V)

while for silicon diodes (eg 1N914, 1N916, 1N4148 or similar) in a 50Ω circuit, it will be:

$$P = \frac{(V + 0.7) \times (V + 0.7)}{2 \times 50}$$

(Forward voltage drop = 0.7V)

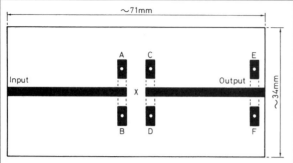

Fig 9.22. (a) Layout of a microstrip and SMD version of the simple milliwatt power meter which will work at 1.3GHz. (b) Photograph of the completed unit *(G3PFR)*

Schottky barrier diodes of different types suitable for microwave use show various forward drops, the value of which can be found from the manufacturers' data.

Using this principle, it is now easy to make up the circuit using glassfibre printed circuit board (PCB) material and modern surface-mounted resistors, capacitors and diodes to construct a load/milliwatt power meter which is effective to at least 2.5GHz. Surface mount devices (SMDs), briefly described earlier, are much smaller than ordinary devices and are made to solder directly to microstrip tracks on a PCB. They literally have no connecting leads, connection being made by soldering to metallised areas at each end of the device. Being very small and lying flat on the board close to an earthed 'ground plane', they are less reactive than standard components with leads. This means that they will work better at higher frequencies. The recommended 1206 size is 0.120in (3.2mm) long and 0.06in (1.6mm) wide – rather small compared to a standard resistor or capacitor!

A PCB layout is shown in Fig 9.22. For this design you can make your own PCB as the dimensions of the

microstrip are not very critical! The PCB has been designed larger than needed so that it will fit inside a Type 7752 tinplate box (Piper Communications) which is $37 \times 74 \times 30$mm. This is a useful size for other small items of test gear too!

The other side of the board is unetched to provide a continuous ground plane. The board is held in place by soldering all round the edge of the ground plane where it meets the tinplate box sides and ends. The PCB is placed so that the input and output connectors are soldered directly to the microstrip line.

The trick is to use a length of 50Ω microstrip transmission line from the input socket to the load, and low-inductance grounding wherever grounding is needed. The length of the line is not critical, although the width is. Low-inductance earthing (grounding) for all components is provided by 1mm circuit pins fitted through small holes very close to the component to be grounded and soldered on both sides of the board, a technique used successfully at 10GHz (see later). The chip resistors are soldered between this line and ground, and there is a small gap in the line to allow fitting of the diode with absolutely minimum lead length (or to fit an SMD diode). The output line does not need to be 50Ω, although it is convenient to make it the same as the input line. Note that the DC output is decoupled by two SMD capacitors close to the diode and by two more near the output socket. Use a coaxial output socket so that a well-screened lead can be taken to the meter to prevent any stray RF pick-up which could upset the accuracy of the readings.

With good-quality 1.6mm (1/16in) epoxy-glassfibre, 1oz double-clad board, the microstrip line should be 2.7mm wide to give an impedance of 50Ω. If you use standard PCB masking tape as an etch resist, the nearest size is 2.5mm. Using this will give a microstrip impedance of about 52Ω, near enough for all practical purposes! This author used an SMA connector at the input (because it matched the connectors on most of the low-power equipment which he wanted to test) and a Belling-Lee (75Ω) TV connector, as the impedance does not matter at the output (which is DC). Alternatively, you could use a BNC socket if you use BNC leads on your other equipment.

1. First make, drill and clean up your board (all holes are 1mm diameter).

2. Fit the 1mm grounding pins with their heads flush to the ground-plane side at positions A–F inclusive. Solder both sides! Cut off any excess pin length on the track side.

3. Mark the centre line along the box sides and ends – this is where the board will fit.

4. At the centre of each end, mark and drill holes for the input and output sockets. The size of these holes

will depend on the type of connectors you decide to use. Fix in place the input socket (gold-plated SMA) by soldering it to the tinplate box end. If you have a big enough soldering iron, you can also solder the BNC (or whatever) connector to the other end. If you use a Belling-Lee socket, this is quite easy as the insulation does not protrude behind the socket body. Either the square-flange or single-hole (round-flange) BNC are a little more difficult, as both have both metal and insulation which protrude behind the surface on which they are mounted. A round, single-hole BNC type is best fitted by soldering a spare socket-nut to the tinplate box end, screwing the socket into place and using another nut to lock it in place. The square-flange type can be soldered directly to the box, but either type of BNC connector will need a 'notch' filing in the PCB to clear the insulation and socket body, and to allow the PCB to sit down directly on the connector spill.

5. You will also need to file a little from the corners of the board where there is a seam in the box and it is a good idea to spend a bit of time making the board a good fit into its box.

6. Once you are satisfied that it is a good fit and that the lids fit well, the corner seams of the box can be soldered.

7. Tack-solder the board into the box.

8. When satisfied that the board is correctly fitted, solder all round the joint between the ground plane and box.

9. Solder the coaxial socket spills to the tracks.

10. Solder the resistors and capacitors in place using a fine soldering iron, very fine solder, a pair of tweezers and a magnifying glass! Use a minimum of solder and heat (solder as quickly as you can), soldering one end first while holding the device in place with the tip of the tweezers or a wooden cocktail stick. This should fix the component in place. Then solder the other side.

11. The diode, whatever type is used, should be fitted last of all. If you use a type with leads, use the shortest leads possible with the body of the diode flat on the board.

Calibration

The DC output voltage can be measured with a multimeter set to a voltage range between 0.5 and 10V. You can construct a calibration curve for the milliwattmeter by calculating the voltages produced at different input powers. You can be sure that the calibration will not be far out. You might even like to write a simple microcomputer program to do the calculation for you! A typical calibration curve is given in Fig 9.23. Alternatively, you might be able to get it calibrated directly (at as high a frequency as possible, say 2.5GHz) at one of the Microwave Round

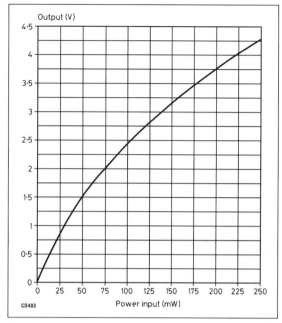

Fig 9.23. Voltage/power calibration curve for the milliwatt power meter

Tables*, or by another amateur who has the necessary test gear. Don't forget that the chip resistors forming the load are only rated at 0.125W (125mW), so that the load will only operate without overheating to 0.25W (250mW).

If you want to measure up to, say, 0.5W (500mW), then there are 0.5W, 50Ω BNC-mounted terminating loads rated to 1GHz or 2W BNC-in, BNC-out 'through loads' rated to 0.5GHz. Both are usable to at least 2GHz without too much inaccuracy. Both can occasionally be found at rallies or are available from RS Components (or Electromail), part numbers 456-251 and 456-150 respectively. There are similar items in the Farnell Electronic Components catalogue.

Using a terminating load together with a BNC T-piece and a BNC 'video mount' (containing a coaxially mounted diode and decoupling) which is sometimes obtainable cheaply from rallies, you can 'build' a power meter without having to construct anything at all! The 'layout' is shown in Fig 9.24. It is used in exactly the same way as the microstrip design just described. A 'through load' is even easier – remove the T-piece and

* Microwave Round Tables are meetings where microwave enthusiasts can discuss technical and operating matters, exchange ideas and equipment, and usually use professional test equipment to align transmitters and receivers. These meetings are held several times a year, usually at a university or other professional laboratory. Details can be obtained from either the *Microwave Newsletter* (available on subscription from RSGB HQ) or from any RSGB Microwave Committee member (see *Radio Communication* or *RSGB Amateur Radio Call Book*).

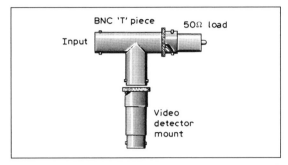

Fig 9.24. A coaxial power meter using ready-made BNC components

simply connect the power input to one end of the load and the video mount to the other.

A simple directional coupler power indicator for 1.3GHz

Fig 9.25 gives the track pattern for a simple directional coupler power indicator for the 1.3GHz band, suitable for powers up to about 50W. It consists of a 50Ω microstrip line connecting the input socket to the output socket. The U-shaped 50Ω line is coupled to the main line. One end is terminated in a matching 50Ω chip resistor while the other end is connected to a decoupled detector diode. RF current flowing in the main line induces a small current in the coupled line. This is detected by the diode and can be indicated on a sensitive multimeter connected to the meter output socket. The insertion loss is small and the coupler can be left in circuit all the time as a forward power indicator. You could add another identical coupled line on the other side of the main line, with the diode and resistor positions interchanged and a second meter, if you wanted to indicate reverse power at the same time.

The board material is the same as that used for the

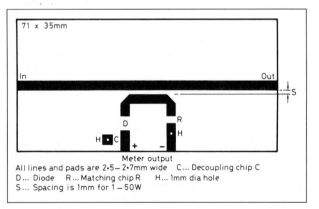

Meter output
All lines and pads are 2·5 – 2·7mm wide   C... Decoupling chip C
D... Diode   R... Matching chip R   H... 1mm dia hole
S... Spacing is 1mm for 1 – 50W

Fig 9.25. PCB track pattern for a simple directional coupler power indicator for 1.3GHz

power meter described earlier and is exactly the same size, so that it will fit in the same way into the same type of tinplate box. The other side of the board is left unetched as a ground plane. The slight mismatch caused by using standard 2.5mm masking tape as an etch-resist is not too important in this piece of equipment: it will still work well enough for most purposes, in this case to measure relative forward power.

Exactly the same methods of construction are used as for the power meter. The input and output sockets could be BNC, TNC, SMA, SMB or SMC, whichever suits the constructor best. The smaller types are easier to use. You may need to make cutouts so that the board will just clear the backs of the sockets. The positions of the board and sockets should be arranged so that the spills of the sockets can be soldered directly onto the microstrip conductor. The board is soldered to the box walls all round its edges and ends. The DC output from the diode detector is decoupled by a 1000pF chip capacitor and taken to any type of feedthrough connector on the side of the box, close to the diode. This author used a miniature BNC coaxial connector so that a screened (coaxial) lead could be taken to the meter. This connector has the advantage that both DC and ground connections are made together and the lead will not pick up any stray RF which might give false readings.

There is no alignment or adjustment to be made – just use it!

Frequency measurements in the range 88MHz to 450MHz

Typical microwave oscillator sources such as the G4DDK-001 (described before) usually start off with crystal frequencies around the 88MHz to 108MHz mark, depending on the application. That should immediately suggest a way of checking that the crystal oscillator stage is functioning correctly – yes, tune it in on an FM broadcast receiver with the antenna disconnected and the squelch switched off! The crystal is unmodulated and the signal will only be detectable by quieting of the hiss. The frequency reading on the tuning scale should be about the same as that of the crystal.

If it appears to be a long way out, the circuit could be self-oscillating at a frequency not controlled by the crystal. If the oscillator is controlled by the crystal, touching the oscillator coil or moving the core slightly will have little effect on the signal heard on the receiver. If it is self-oscillating, there will be a large change of frequency when the coil is touched or the core moved.

Checking the frequencies of the multiplier stages which follow the oscillator is a little more difficult! These frequencies might lie anywhere within

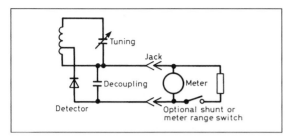

Fig 9.26. Circuit of absorption wavemeters (G3LYP)

the range 150 to 2500MHz. The simplest solution is to use absorption wavemeters. It is difficult (but possible) to build a single wavemeter covering the whole of this range and so it is better to build two or three covering, for instance, 60 to 160MHz, 150 to 300MHz and 250 to 2500MHz.

The first two are easily and inexpensively made. Fig 9.26 gives the circuit of both. Either consists of a coil or loop of wire, a variable tuning capacitor, a diode to detect the RF, a decoupling capacitor and a meter to indicate resonance. Note that the diode is tapped into the tuned circuit. The tapping point is a compromise between obtaining enough signal to give a decent meter reading and reducing the Q of the circuit to an extent which affects the sharpness (or resolution) of the tuning. The use of a sensitive meter, for example 10 to 50 or 100µA, helps in this respect.

The form of construction, suggested by Mike Scott, G3LYP, is shown in Fig 9.27 and 9.28. Each is built on a piece of 0.1in thick single-clad PCB material cut to roughly the dimensions shown: the sizes are not critical, except you'll find difficulty in coupling the wavemeter to the circuit under test if the wavemeter is too large. Again, it is possible to use thinner (¹/₁₆in) board but this is less rigid.

Etching patterns are also given in the diagrams; again, these are not really critical and you could produce the tracks by cutting through the copper with a sharp blade

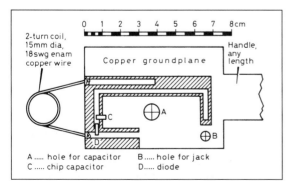

Fig 9.27. Layout and track pattern for absorption wavemeter covering approximately 60 to 160MHz

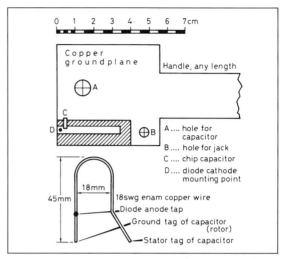

Fig 9.28. Layout and track pattern for absorption wavemeter covering approximately 150 to 300MHz

and stripping off the *unwanted* copper by applying a hot soldering iron to it and peeling it off while the board bonding is soft. The tuning capacitors used by G3LYP were small 50pF types with ⁵/₁₆in bushes and ⁷/₃₂in shafts, obtained from a rally. One was used 'as is' for the 60MHz to 160MHz version. For the other, half the rotor and stator plates were carefully removed by gentle twisting with a pair of pliers.

The copper track forms part of the tuned circuit in the lower-frequency unit and the junction between the track and the rest of the coil forms a convenient tapping point for the diode. To keep the stray capacitance to a minimum, the loop on the higher frequency unit is soldered directly to the tags on the tuning capacitor, with the diode soldered between the loop, about ¹/₂in from the ground end, and a track on the PCB. The tuning capacitors are mounted on the track side of the board and a paper calibration scale on the other side. Once calibrated, the scale can be protected by a coat of varnish or lacquer.

To keep the units small, a 3.5mm jack socket is fitted and used to connect a screened lead to a separate box containing a suitable meter – either a multimeter or an inexpensive miniature panel meter, again often obtainable from rallies and often with a sensitivity of 50 or 75µA.

Once completed, how do you calibrate the wavemeters? This is best done with a dip oscillator or signal generator, maybe at a Microwave Round Table for instance, or by enlisting help from another local amateur. Calibration does not have to be exact because what you are mainly interested in is whether the stage being measured is within, say, 10MHz of where it ought to be. In other words, you need to know whether that stage you've

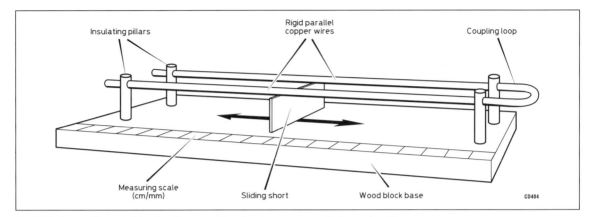

Fig 9.29. General layout of Lecher lines used for direct measurement of wavelength

just peaked up by measuring voltage drop across an emitter resistor is doubling and not simply amplifying or tripling! Failing help, you could use Lecher lines to calibrate a tuneable oscillator which is, in turn, used to calibrate your wavemeters.

Lecher lines for approximate frequency measurement

Above about 100MHz or so, it is practical to directly measure the *wavelength* at which a transmitter is working by using a pair of parallel wires or rods known as 'Lecher lines' (pronounced 'lekker'), spaced about an inch (25mm) apart. The method, used with care, is accurate enough to tell you whether the transmitter output is in the band, that is, it can detect if you have tuned the transmitter output to the right harmonic or not. It can also detect harmonics and is the simplest and most fundamental way to measure frequencies.

The wires or rods form an open-wire 'transmission line' into which the transmitter output can be fed by means of a coupling loop or a short length of coaxial cable. A shorting 'bridge' (thin bar or sharp metal strip) can be slid along the lines as needed and a meter and diode detector are also coupled into the line.

The general layout of the Lecher lines is shown in Fig 9.29. Starting with the shorting bridge near the coupling end of the line, the bridge is slowly slid along the lines towards the open end until a point of maximum current is indicated on the meter. This position is carefully noted on the scale and the bridge slid slowly further along the line until the next similar position is found. This position is also noted. This should be carefully repeated several times until you get the same readings of distance each time. The distance between the two points will be half the wavelength at which the transmitter is operating.

The wavelength can be used to calculate the frequency, using the formula:

$$\text{Frequency (MHz)} = \frac{15,000}{D}$$

where D is the distance between peaks in centimetres. For example, if the distance measured is approximately 11.6cm (116mm), then the frequency is:

$$\text{Frequency} = \frac{15,000}{11.6} = 1293\text{MHz (approximately)}$$

There are many ways of making Lecher lines. Two ways are described here. The first is a simplified version of a design due to Mike Scott, G3LYP, and is shown in Fig 9.30. None of the dimensions is critical. The base is made from a piece of hardwood about 1m long, 100mm wide and thick enough to be rigid. A wooden or plastic metre rule, graduated in millimetres and centimetres, is fixed (screwed or glued) at one edge of the baseboard. A strip of hardwood of similar width and thickness to the metre rule is fixed on the other edge, leaving a shallow 'trough' about 40mm wide down the middle of the baseboard.

Two fairly thick tinned copper wires (about 3.2mm or 10swg) are mounted about 30mm apart, about 25 or 30mm above the base of the centre trough, and are tensioned between their mountings by means of an adjustable plastic (polythene or similar) insulating strip at the open end of the lines. The coupled end of the lines is fixed by means of a stiff bracket.

A small block of hardwood is cut to slide smoothly in the trough. A sheet of thin, but stiff, copper is fixed in a saw cut in the top surface of the sliding block as shown, so that it is in contact with the underside of both the lines.

You could make the lines a lot shorter than this, depending on how low a frequency (or, rather, how long a wavelength!) you want to measure. At a metre long you can measure frequencies as low as about 150MHz; shortened to half a metre, measurements down to about 300MHz are possible.

An alternative and far simpler method of construction

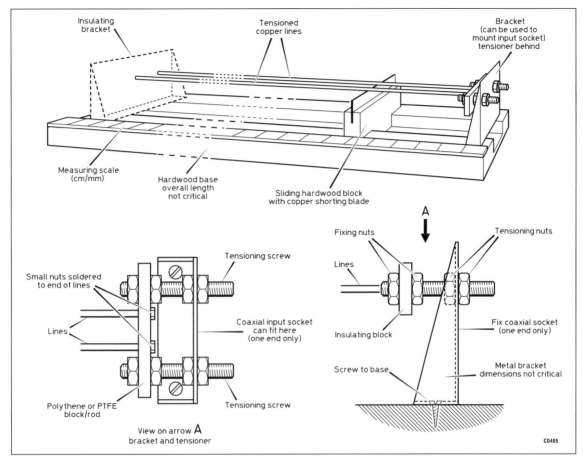

Fig 9.30. Construction of Lecher lines *(G3LYP)*

was suggested by John Tye, G4BYV. This is illustrated in the two photographs in Fig 9.31. Here, use is made of an N-type T-connector with two socket ends and one plug end, a square-flange N-type socket and two lengths of tinned or silver-plated copper rod. The rods are soldered directly to the centre pin and one of the fixing holes of the N-type socket and are supported by means of two blocks of plastic (in this case Perspex), one at each end of the lines. The 'plug' arm of the T-connector is modified by unscrewing the centre pin, cutting a little off the screwed end and soldering a small metal disc on the cut end. A small disc of thin polythene or PTFE is placed on the end of the disc and the modified centre conductor pushed back into the body of the connector. The disc forms a small capacitor to couple into the line and the pin is held in place by screwing in the N-type socket soldered to the line. One of the T-connector sockets is used to couple to the transmitter to be tested, and the other connects to an N-Type detector mount as shown in Fig 9.31. For very approximate measurements, there is

no need for a measuring scale to be fixed to the lines and the shorting contact can be the blade of a small insulated screwdriver, or any other insulated metal strip.

A wavemeter for the range 250MHz to 2.5GHz

A wide-range wavemeter was described in Volume 2 of the RSGB *Microwave Handbook*. This version is simpler and needs no machined parts, using instead copper 'plumbing' parts which are available from any DIY store. You will need the bits and pieces listed in Table 9.4. *Note that none of the dimensions given is critical.*

1. Cut the copper pipe to length, using either a hacksaw or a pipe cutter.
2. Square off the ends and remove 'lips' or burrs.
3. Mark and cut the socket mounting and clearance holes as shown in Fig 9.32(a). To be sure that the holes are correctly placed, drill through *both* walls in one operation. Remove burrs.

Fig 9.31. Construction of Lecher Lines *(G4BYV)*. Left: general view. Lower left: close-up of T-connector end of lines. Below: test set-up

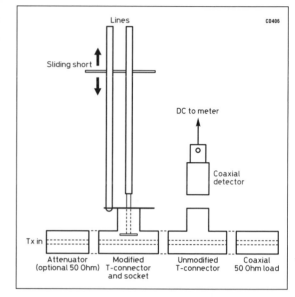

4. Prepare the copper stop-end fitting by drilling as shown in Fig 9.32(b). Remove burrs.
5. Fit the shaft bushing into the centre hole as shown in Fig 9.32(c), and tighten the nuts firmly.
6. Make sure that the copper pipe is clean and bright, both inside and outside. Clean it, if necessary, with a wet, soapy panscrub or wire wool. Wash and dry it.
7. Fit countersunk bolts in the four smaller holes in the copper pipe, fixing them in place with clean brass half-nuts.
8. Using a fine blowtorch flame and a little resin-cored solder, carefully solder the nuts and bolts in place on the pipe. The nuts will form a firm mounting for the socket flanges.
9. Fit the prepared stop end, aligning the small holes with the socket mounting screws, as shown in Fig 9.32(d).
10. Solder the stop end in place using the blowtorch flame

Table 9.4. Components list for the wide-range wavemeter

12in (305mm) length of standard 22mm OD copper pipe
14in (355mm) length of ¼in (6mm) brass rod
22mm 'Yorkshire' (self-soldering) stop end
Bushing for ¼in (6mm) shaft, at least ½in (13mm) long, preferably made from brass and maybe salvaged from an old radio set or wirewound 'volume control'. Alternatively, the RS Components type 509-816 split collet 'Spindle Lock' may be used.
Control knob with ¼in (6mm) bush
25mm ×25mm piece of 3mm thick (not critical) PTFE or polythene sheet
Two flange-mounting coaxial sockets (eg BNC, SMA or Belling-Lee. The impedance does not matter – Belling-Lee are easiest to use)
Two coaxial plugs, to match sockets
Four 6BA (or 3mm) countersunk bolts, ¼in (6mm) long
6BA (or 3mm) cheesehead bolt, ¼in (6mm) long
6BA (or 3mm) cheesehead bolt, 1in (25mm) long
Four nuts and plain washers to fit above bolts
Four brass half-nuts, approx 1.6mm thick – see text
A few inches of 20swg (0.7mm) tinned copper wire, resin-cored solder and small-flamed gas blowtorch

around the rim on the stop end. You should see the solder run around the joint when the stop end and pipe are hot enough.

11. Remove the flame and allow the pipe and stop end to cool completely without being disturbed. This completes mechanical construction of the wavemeter body.
12. Cut two 3in (76mm) lengths of the tinned copper wire and bend one end of each to fit tightly round the solder spills of the two sockets.
13. Align each wire with two opposite socket mounting holes, as shown in Fig 9.32(e), then solder each wire to its socket spill. Allow to cool.
14. The next steps need a little juggling! Feed one of the wires through one of the socket clearance holes on the wavemeter body and down through the adjacent small hole on the stop end, placing the mounting holes of the socket over the mounting screws on the body.
15. Fix in place with a washer and nut fitted to both screws.
16. Once in place, straighten the wire by pulling it through the hole and then bend it over at right-angles where it protrudes from the hole, and then cut off the excess.
17. Repeat steps 14 to 16 for the other socket.
18. When both are in place, solder the wires to the stop end, using as little heat as possible.

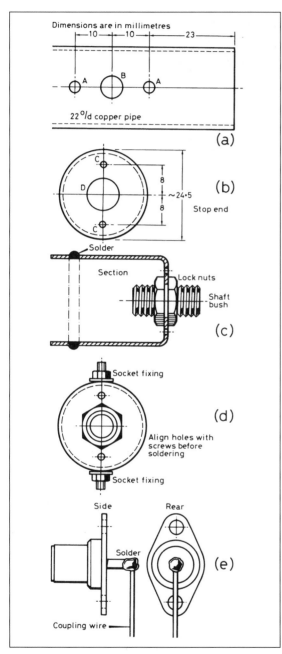

Fig 9.32. Construction of a wavemeter covering 250MHz to 2.5GHz. (a) Drilling coaxial socket mounting holes. (b) Drilling the stop-end. (c) Fitting the shaft bushing. (d) Aligning the stop-end. (e) Position of the coupling wires on the sockets

19. Square-off the ends of the brass rod.
20. Drill a 2.3mm (for 6BA) or 2.5mm (for 3mm) hole, about 5mm deep, centrally in one end, and tap it to take a screw.

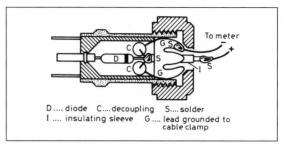

Fig 9.33. Construction of a simple coaxial detector for the wide-range wavemeter

21. Take the piece of PTFE or polythene and mark the centre, using diagonals.
22. Mark a circle of 20mm diameter and cut a disc a little larger than this, using a fret-saw or sharp knife (care!).
23. Drill the marked centre hole to just clear the bolt you are going to use to fix the disc to the rod.
24. Fix the disc to a long, say 1in (25mm), bolt, using one or two nuts and washers, and clamp the bolt in the chuck of a hand-drill which is in turn clamped in a vice.
25. Using a file or abrasive paper, you can now 'turn' the disc to exactly the right size to be a smooth, sliding fit into the wavemeter body. The disc helps keep the rod central in the cavity.
26. When satisfied, fix it in place on the tapped end of the brass rod and fit the other end of the brass rod down through the body and through the shaft bushing.
27. Align the disc with the open end of the body. This leaves enough rod at the opposite end to attach the control knob against the outer end of the shaft bushing: if there is too much, cut off the excess to match the depth of the knob which then acts as an 'end-stop'.
28. Make off one of the coaxial plugs with a short length (say 6in) of coaxial cable and solder a single-turn probe loop, say 6 to 8mm in diameter, between the inner and outer of the cable at the free end of the cable. Alternatively, fix another plug suitable for connection to the equipment to be aligned.
29. Make a detector by taking the other plug and soldering a diode and decoupling capacitors, as shown in Fig 9.33, inside the plug.
30. Attach a sensitive meter (for example 10 to 100μA) between the plug body (earth) and the detector output.
31. Plug the detector into one socket and the probe loop into the other – it doesn't matter which!

Using the wavemeter

The wavemeter works as follows: power is fed into the cavity from the probe loop. When the centre rod is a

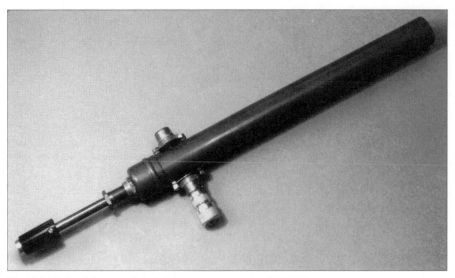

Fig 9.34. Photo of the completed wide-range wavemeter *(G3PFR)*

in length is $^1/_2\lambda$, from which the frequency can be calculated; the wavemeter becomes self-calibrating.

Place the loop close to the circuit to be measured and slowly withdraw the knob of the wavemeter. At some point the meter will indicate power. Note the position and mark the shaft with the frequency, if known. Continue withdrawing the rod, looking for a second response. If there is only one response, this will be the $^1/_4\lambda$ mode. In very-low-power circuits, it might be impossible to get a meter reading; in this case, try monitoring the emitter voltage or collector current of the stage, looking for a small change in current or voltage as the wavemeter resonates and absorbs power. Alternatively, the wavemeter may be connected to the output socket of the equipment to be aligned, if necessary via a matched (50Ω) attenuator, to couple enough power into the wavemeter to give adequate indication.

Made in this way, the wavemeter should cover from about 250MHz to 2.5GHz. A photograph of the completed wavemeter is shown in Fig 9.34. The range could be extended to lower frequencies by increasing the length of the body and resonator rod, leaving all other dimensions unchanged.

quarter or three-quarters wavelength (λ) long (inside the cavity), it resonates and absorbs power from the coupling line. Maximum current occurs at the earthed end of the rod and maximum voltage at the 'open' end. At resonance, some power is transferred to the detector coupling line, where it is detected to produce a DC current which is indicated by the meter.

Frequencies can be marked on the brass rod with an indelible marker or *light* scribe mark. More elaborately, as suggested by Mike Scott, G3LYP, and the *Microwave Handbook*, the wavemeter can be mounted on a wooden base carrying a calibrated (millimetre) scale, but this is not really necessary! Where the $^3/_4\lambda$ resonant length is less than the physical length of the wavemeter body, you will find *two* resonances: at $^3/_4\lambda$ and $^1/_4\lambda$. The difference

Chapter 10

Transmitters and test equipment for the 10GHz band

Waveguides and coaxial lines

The 10GHz band is the only Novice band where you may come across waveguides – so what are they? Waveguides are metal tubes (usually rectangular, but may be round or elliptical) which are used to carry microwaves in the same way as lower frequencies are carried by coaxial lines. This is not to say that you can't use coaxial lines at 10GHz – you can, but more of the microwave power is lost than in the same length of waveguide and you have to be very careful what size of cable is used. If the cable is too large, then losses increase more rapidly than expected due to an effect known as 'over-moding'.

Waveguide is made in many different sizes, each used to carry a particular band of frequencies. Much 10GHz equipment was until recently built in waveguide-16 (WG16). This is the most suitable rectangular guide for use at 10GHz. It has outside measurements of 1in (25.4mm) by 0.5in (12.7mm). The inside measurements are 0.9in (22.9mm) by 0.4in (10.2mm). It is available most commonly in copper, brass and aluminium. It can be obtained from a number of sources, either new or secondhand on the surplus market.

You will most likely use short lengths of waveguide to connect either a transmitter or a receiver to an antenna. You might also buy surplus professional waveguide components, used to make up test equipment, from rallies. Lengths of waveguide, or individual components, are fixed together by metal flanges. You might come across two shapes of standard flange, one rectangular and the other round. The measurements of each are given in Fig 10.1. Rectangular flanges are less expensive than the round type and need only four bolts to fasten them together. You could make flanges of this type yourself from thick brass plate cut, drilled and filed to fit the waveguide. The 'boss' on the rear of commercial flanges helps accurate fitting to waveguide, but is not essential to their use.

The round types need a pair of special screw-coupling/locating rings which make them 'quick-release'. They are very useful where you may often need to attach or detach different pieces of equipment – to or from a common antenna feed, for example.

Plain flanges of either type have a shallow groove in them which takes a rubber ring to provide a weather seal. The plain type is designed to fit flush with the end of the waveguide. Choke flanges, of either type, have a recessed face and another, deeper groove (other than that for the seal) in it. This groove and the recessed face form a quarter-wave choke which reduces leakage from the joint so that we do not have to rely on metal-to-metal contact to prevent loss of microwave energy from the waveguide. Choke flanges are designed to be matched with a plain flange to provide a 'leak-proof' RF connection.

You might sometimes find sections of flexible or flexible and twistable waveguide in surplus equipment which could be used to align rigid waveguides. You may also come across elliptical, corrugated semi-flexible waveguide. It is seldom used in amateur installations because it is very expensive. You may also find rigid bends, twists, T-shaped junctions and several other different components, most of which can be useful for testing.

Losses in waveguide, coaxial lines and connectors

Table 10.1 shows the losses at 10GHz in waveguide and coaxial lines. It is obvious why coaxial lines are not often used at 10GHz and why, when they are, they are used only in short lengths! RG402 is often used in very short lengths to connect individual pieces of equipment together and LDF4-50 is sometimes used in short runs between equipment and an antenna.

Table 10.2 shows the extra losses from coaxial connectors at 10GHz. Again, you can see that if a lot of coaxial connectors are used, quite high losses occur – use as few as you can! Where you do need to use them, try to use SMA types, as these are best at this frequency and should be used for 10GHz circuits which are built on PCBs (see later).

Advantages and disadvantages of waveguide

There are several advantages to using waveguide, other than its lower transmission losses explained before. One is that components can be built on or into short sections of guide which can then be bolted together to form

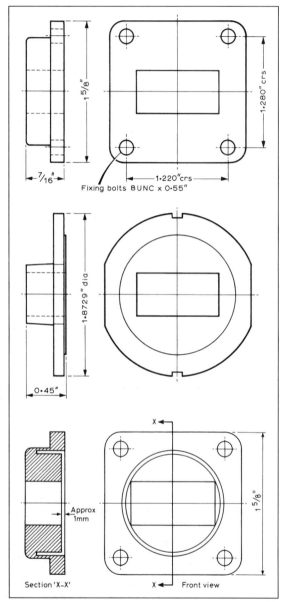

Fig 10.1. Three types of flange for waveguide-16 (WG16). Top: square plain flange. Middle: round plain flange. Bottom: square choke flange

Table 10.1. Losses in waveguide and coaxial lines at 10GHz

Type	Loss (dB) per 100ft (31m)
Brass waveguide-16	5.5
Copper waveguide-16	2.2
UR43 coaxial (flexible)	>100
UR67 coaxial (flexible)	≫100
LDF2-50 coaxial (semi-flexible)	14.0
LDF4-50 coaxial (semi-flexible)	12.0
RG402 coaxial (semi-rigid)	45.0
RG401 coaxial (semi-rigid)	30.0

Table 10.2. Losses in coaxial connectors at 10GHz

Type	Loss (dB) per connector
BNC	Not suitable
N-Type	0.5
TNC	0.5
SMA	0.3
SMB	Not suitable
SMC	0.6

three-screw tuner is shown in Fig 10.2 and consists of three screws mounted on the centre line of the broad face of the waveguide. After adjustment they are fixed in place by locknuts. The screws may be mounted anywhere along the waveguide but are best near to the component to be matched. The screws can be supported better by soldering a piece of thick brass plate to the face of the waveguide before drilling and tapping the screw holes. 'Heavy' soldering like this is quite easy, provided that the metal to be soldered is clean, good cored solder is used and a gas 'torch' is used instead of a soldering iron. You'll almost certainly need someone to show you how to do this safely and you'll need to practise on a few scrap bits of brass or copper until you can make good joints!

The three-screw tuner can be set during final testing of the equipment – see later. You'll usually find that only one, or perhaps two, of the three screws will have a

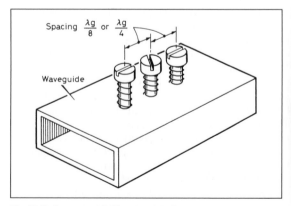

Fig 10.2. A waveguide three-screw tuner

complete equipment. Another is that tuning and matching of waveguide is easy. Finally, many ready-made precision waveguide components such as bends, twists, couplers, wavemeters, variable attenuators, detectors, mixers and oscillators are available cheaply as professional surplus.

Matching is easy using a three-screw tuner, which acts rather like an 'antenna tuner' at lower frequencies. A

significant effect. The screws should be inserted the smallest amount needed to achieve a good match. If the screws have to be inserted well into the waveguide then the component is probably a bad match; if none of them have any beneficial effect, then the component is probably already well matched.

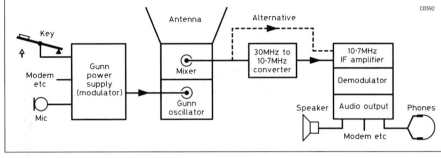

Fig 10.3. Block diagram of a Gunn oscillator transmitter (and receiver) at 10GHz, using a surplus Doppler 'in-line' oscillator/mixer unit

The main disadvantages to using waveguide are the cost, weight, size, rigidity and the fact that making equipment or components in waveguide involves a lot of metalwork and heavy soldering!

Simple wide-band (FM) transmitters for 10GHz

The simplest transmitter which you can build consists of a waveguide cavity Gunn oscillator and a variable voltage, stabilised, modulated bias (power) supply. A simple transmitter may only generate 10 or 20mW output, but this is enough to allow wide-band communication at the least over short obstructed paths and longer unobstructed paths, and sometimes over very long distances.

Gunn oscillator bias supplies are simple, low-voltage supplies which are easily modulated to produce good-quality FM signals. The simplicity and low cost of such equipment has made the band very popular, especially with novices to microwave techniques. A block diagram of a Gunn transmitter is shown in Fig 10.3. Gunn power supplies and modulators are described before Gunn oscillators because you won't be able to test an oscillator without a suitable power supply!

Safety

Although the power output of surplus Gunn oscillators is only a few milliwatts, **you should never, ever look closely down the open end of the oscillator or waveguide while the device is working.** For one thing, you won't see anything happening and, for another, it could damage your eyes. Although this is very unlikely, you should learn that RF energy, no matter what its frequency, when 'concentrated' (as at the end of a waveguide, or by an antenna) can cause burns anywhere on the body. Your eyes are one of the most delicate and sensitive parts of the body, so don't take any risks!

Gunn power supplies and modulators

Gunn oscillators can be frequency modulated by using an effect called 'frequency pushing' where the frequency depends on the supply voltage. The frequency of the oscillator is mainly set by the cavity size. The cavity can be tuned mechanically by means of a screw inserted into it. The frequency can also be varied over a small range around the frequency set by the tuning screw by varying the DC conditions on the Gunn diode ('frequency pushing').

This frequency-pushing effect is, or can be, one of the main sources of FM noise on the carrier. Unless the bias (power) supply is free from noise and spurious (unwanted) oscillation, then the generated carrier will be 'dirty' in terms of FM noise sidebands. Even with a well-designed and decoupled bias supply, there will still be some FM noise present, arising from random variations in the Gunn device itself. There may also be some AM noise present, also coming from random variations in the device output.

These effects are less in a high-Q oscillator; the surplus oscillators recommended later are high-Q devices. You will still need to be sure that the bias supply is clean and free from spurious noise!

Where you need the very best performance, proper screening of the entire unit – taking the oscillator and bias supply together as being a unit, rather than the oscillator on its own – will reduce noise further. It is a good idea to put both the bias supply and the oscillator (or oscillator/ mixer, as may be) in one screened enclosure, rather than feeding the oscillator from a 'remote' source via a length of screened cable.

In a simple home station, it may be better to go for slightly poorer performance so that you can avoid the use of waveguide by putting the oscillator next to the antenna and running the modulated power supply up a coaxial line from the power supply in the 'shack' as shown in Fig 10.4.

A Gunn bias supply consists of a stabilised supply controlled by a variable voltage regulator. The modulator is simply some means of putting a few tens or hundreds of millivolts of 'audio' voltage (tone or speech) upon this bias. Many suitable circuits have been designed and published by amateurs.

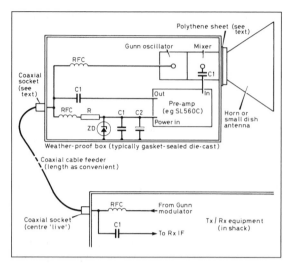

Fig 10.4. Masthead installation of a wide-band transmitter (and receiver). This allows one coaxial feeder to be used for feeding modulated DC up to the Gunn transmitter and to bring down the receiver intermediate frequency to the main receiver

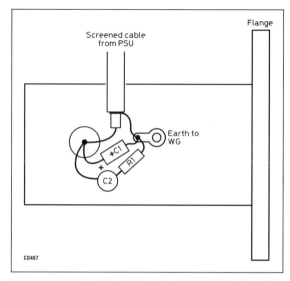

Fig 10.5. Resistor and capacitor network wired directly across the Gunn connection to prevent parasitic oscillations. C1: 1µF, 16V electrolytic or tantalum bead; C2: 10nF disc ceramic; R1: 33Ω

Most small 10GHz Gunn devices giving between 5 and 50mW output need a bias supply between about 6 and 9V at a current of up to roughly 150mA. Building any of the following circuits is not particularly critical, although you must take care with layout to prevent unwanted instability or noise pick-up, for the reasons given before.

It is a good idea to put decoupling components on both the Gunn terminal and in the power supply. The network shown in Fig 10.5, connected directly across the Gunn, is recommended.

Gunn supply/modulator circuits have been built on Veroboard and even using 'bird's nest' construction on small pieces of plain PCB material. A much neater circuit can be built on a small PCB. Although this is not really necessary, a layout and track pattern is given later – this time it is possible for you to make your own PCB!

When completed and tested, you should check the circuit for oscillation. This type of circuit sometimes oscillates at high frequency, often up to several hundred kilohertz or even a few megahertz. The easiest way of checking is to look at the output on an oscilloscope. If instability is seen, the cure is usually to fit a small capacitor from the base of the regulator transistor, or the input and output of the IC, to earth. If you don't have an oscilloscope, the simple test circuit shown in Fig 10.6, due to Phil Schorah, GW3PPF, can be used. Any meter reading indicates the presence of spurious oscillation. Touching different parts of the circuit with the point of a small screwdriver may temporarily stop the oscillation and additional decoupling should be added at that point until the meter reading disappears.

A Gunn power supply/modulator with short-circuit protection

Fig 10.7 shows the basic circuit of a stabilised variable bias supply which was originally designed for the London 10GHz beacon GB3LBH (now no longer operating). It uses a 7805 positive voltage integrated circuit (IC) regulator often used in computer equipment to supply a fixed 5V supply to logic circuits. It will supply up to 1A when used with a suitable heatsink and has built-in short-circuit and thermal protection. Although the regulator was designed for a fixed output, by fitting a 'pedestal' resistor between connection C and earth, the output voltage can be increased up to within 2.5V of the input voltage, by an amount equal to the voltage drop across this resistor. The maximum input voltage to the regulator is 25V. The resistor is also a convenient way to apply modulation to the output voltage, as shown.

The basic circuit has been used by Steve Davies, G4KNZ, as the basis for the design described next. The

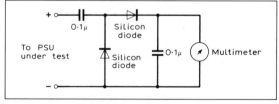

Fig 10.6. Simple test circuit for checking for the presence of high-frequency parasitic oscillations in a Gunn power supply unit (GW3PPF)

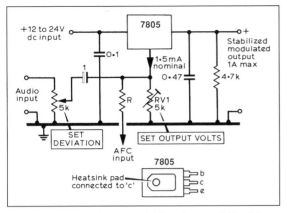

Fig 10.7. Basic circuit for a variable-voltage stabilised Gunn PSU

circuit is given in Fig 10.8 together with all the component values. The layout of the components is given in Fig 10.9, together with heatsink details. The PCB track pattern is given at exact size in Fig 10.10. The top surface of the board is a ground plane to provide good screening.

A single-stage microphone amplifier provides a gain of up to about 10 times and is suitable for use with medium-impedance microphones. The tone generator is a two-transistor multivibrator which can be keyed on and off for CW. Modulation from the microphone amplifier or tone generator is applied to the common terminal of the regulator IC via a capacitor, and the level required

depends on the Gunn voltage (and Gunn diode) but is typically from 10 to 100mV peak-to-peak. The output is variable in the range 6 to 9V. Although the IC is protected against short-circuits, the heatsink used is quite small and the IC will not stand a short-circuit indefinitely. The IC does not actually require a heatsink for the current normally drawn by a low-power Gunn diode. However, it is a good idea to provide limited heatsinking capacity to guard against short-term overload. Several extra decoupling capacitors and resistors have been added to prevent noise on the power supply or tone from the tone generator reaching the microphone amplifier or the Gunn diode. A diode could be included at the power input to protect against accidental supply reversal. Every attempt has been made to keep the circuit simple but with excellent performance.

The circuit is etched onto one side of a double-clad board (Fig 10.10). The other side is unetched and all earth connections are made to this ground plane. Where component leads need to pass through the board un-earthed, the simplest method for the home constructor is to remove a small circle of copper using a drill bit (twisted in the fingers) or a Verotool of the type designed to remove track from Veroboard. Do this *after* the component holes have been drilled and the board cleaned up. The regulator IC will need to be electrically isolated from its heatsink if the sink is screwed down to the PCB. A dab of heatsink grease and an insulator bush assembly is used to do this.

Construction is simple, and in this design any order of

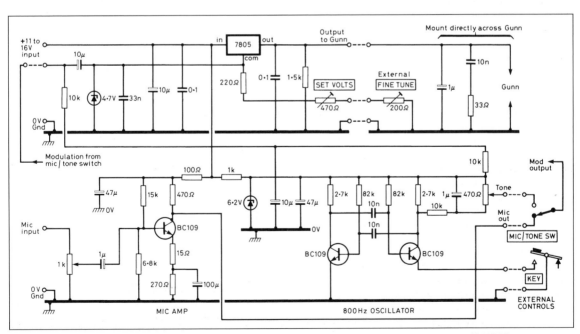

Fig 10.8. Circuit of a complete Gunn PSU/modulator, with microphone amplifier and tone generator (*G4KNZ*)

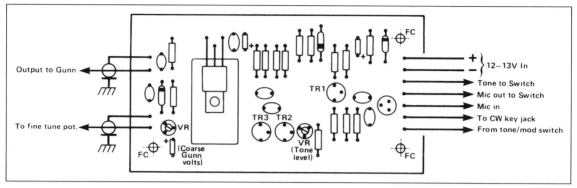

Fig 10.9(a). Component layout for the G4KNZ Gunn PSU/modulator

Fig 10.9(b). Photograph of the completed unit, housed in a die-cast box (G3PFR)

assembly can be used. Testing consists of checking the range of output with a voltmeter. The FINE TUNE potentiometer should be first set to mid-travel and then the 470Ω trimmer set to give the desired output voltage. The FINE TUNE control should then give a voltage swing of about ±1V around this preset value. This control can be a multiturn potentiometer with a calibrated drive; this can later be calibrated directly in frequency. This will give you a guide to the oscillator frequency after the Gunn mechanical tuning screw and operating voltage have been set to the required values.

After testing it is a good idea to check the circuit for oscillation (although this has not proved to be a problem with this particular circuit) by looking at the output on an oscilloscope or by using the simple test circuit already described. The completed board is best mounted in a

screened box close to the Gunn unit to avoid noise or signal pick-up and the incoming power supply may need extra off-board decoupling for the same reason. A short, screened lead should be used to connect the bias supply to the Gunn oscillator.

Measurements made on the prototype circuit gave the following results:

- Tone frequency 830Hz (this may vary with component tolerance).
- Tone output level 100mV (max)
- Microphone amplifier output level 100mV (max) for 10mV input.
- Response −6dB at 100Hz and 25kHz.

Using a Mullard CL8630 Gunn oscillator at a bias voltage of 7V, 150kHz deviation was obtained with a modulation voltage of 30mV p-p at the regulator common terminal.

Fast-scan ATV

If you use the circuits described so far, transmission is limited to 'speech frequency' modes; that is, with the

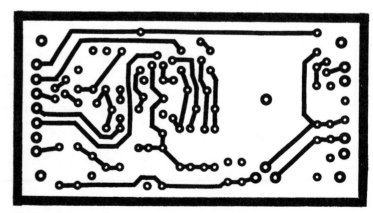

Fig 10.10. PCB track pattern (exact size) for the G4KNZ Gunn PSU/modulator

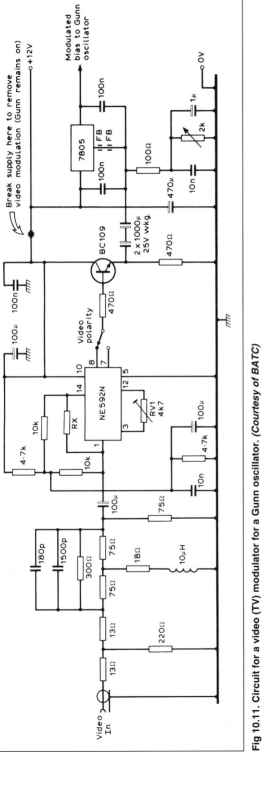

Fig 10.11. Circuit for a video (TV) modulator for a Gunn oscillator. (Courtesy of BATC)

modulating signals in the audio spectrum from a few tens of hertz to perhaps 20kHz. This includes normal speech, tone-modulated CW and tone-modulated frequency shift keying (AFSK) modes such as slow-scan TV (SSTV), packet radio and teletype (RTTY). To transmit full-definition, fast-scan FM TV (FMTV) the modulator circuits must be able to handle bandwidths of several megahertz without distortion or frequency roll-off.

You can find ideas for fast-scan and slow-scan (SSTV) amateur TV equipment on both the 1.3 and 10GHz bands in various British Amateur Television Club (BATC) publications, including *The ATV Compendium*. Anyone interested in ATV should consider joining BATC, which is an affiliated society of the RSGB. BATC publishes an excellent journal called *CQ-TV* four times a year for its members (see Appendix 2).

Most amateur TV activity takes place either in the 1.3GHz or 10GHz bands. A TV transmitter for the 1.3GHz band has not been described in this book since the construction of a suitable phase-locked circuit is more difficult and expensive than a TV transmitter for the 10GHz band.

Due to the much wider bandwidth of the TV signal, the received signal-to-noise ratio (S/N) over a given path will be less than with a WBFM speech transmitter. Even so, on the 10GHz band, distances of up to 100km over line-of-sight paths have been covered with excellent picture quality.

With the bandwidth available on the 10GHz band, there is less need for slow-scan TV except as a way of improving S/N on longer transmission paths using a narrow-band transmitter.

BATC publishes a handbook entitled *The Slow-Scan Companion*; all the techniques and equipment described in the book are suitable for the microwave bands. They also produce PCBs for many of their published circuits. The circuit which follows was originally published by BATC and is included with their permission.

A TV modulator for Gunn oscillators

The circuit given in Fig 10.11 is one of the simplest ways of modulating a Gunn oscillator with a composite video signal, for example, from an ex-security TV camera or a video camcorder. No particular precautions are needed in its construction. The circuit uses an easily available, inexpensive video amplifier IC. The input stage of the IC is designed to have external components fitted to pins 3 and 12 so that the circuit can act as a high-pass, low-pass or band-pass filter. In this case, the external components are chosen to give standard (CCIR) pre-emphasis. The completed modulator should be housed in the same box as the Gunn oscillator so that lead length is kept to a minimum.

The actual modulator is the 7805 regulator circuit used

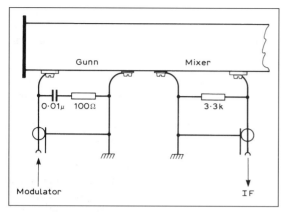

Fig 10.12. Anti-parasitic decoupling of the Gunn terminal for TV modulation *(BATC)*

before, and adapted for this use. About 50mV of video signal, derived from the 1V p-p (standard) input signal, should appear on the Gunn bias voltage if examined using an oscilloscope. If this level of signal cannot be obtained by varying the 4.7kΩ gain control, then the value of Cx can be adjusted on test until a satisfactory range of control is achieved. The normal anti-parasitic components should be fitted directly on the Gunn terminal as shown in Fig 10.12.

The ATV Compendium describes a different circuit which allows modulation with a sound sub-carrier as well as a composite video signal. A suitable PCB is available from BATC for this more advanced circuit.

Using 'surplus' Gunn oscillators

Large numbers of 'doppler intruder alarm' Gunn oscillators and some oscillator/mixers have come onto the surplus market. Many are dual-cavity side-by-side or 'piggyback' types and are not really suitable for amateur use. There are, however, a few types around which you can use directly and effectively.

An oscillator of excellent design which is still in production and available from normal commercial sources, as well as surplus, is the Mullard CL8630 Gunn oscillator. At first glance the waveguide appears too small for a 10GHz Gunn device, but the flange matches a square WG16 flange and it is designed so that there is a step in waveguide size at this point. This step prevents pulling of the oscillator frequency with changing load – the frequency is remarkably insensitive to the presence of objects (for example, hands) near the open flange, unlike many other designs tested. The oscillators are normally on a frequency of 10.687GHz, but the tuning screw can be adjusted to pull the frequency down into the amateur band. Usually it is possible to pull them down to 10.1GHz, but there will certainly be no trouble in using them at 10.3 to 10.4GHz. The oscillator is shown in Fig 10.13

and some data for it is also given there. No modifications are needed when the oscillator is used as a fixed-tuned transmitter, only retuning.

Another oscillator which has been found to be satisfactory is made by Solfan in the USA. No technical details are available. As can be seen in Fig 10.14, this is a heavy die-cast unit. It is tuned by means of a large brass screw and the frequency again is around 10.68GHz. There are two slightly different types which differ only in the presence or absence of an additional tuning/matching screw just inside the open end of the cavity. You can retune either type into the amateur band by adjustment of the main tuning screw. If the oscillator is to be used as a fixed-tuned transmitter, no modification is needed, only retuning.

There is a simple modification to make the Solfan oscillator tuneable, as follows.

1. Adjacent to the Gunn decoupling disc there is a solder tag, held in place by a screw, which is used to earth an electrolytic bypass capacitor. Remove the screw and solder tag.
2. Carefully remove the rear plate, which is held in place by four screws, and place it on one side. Do *not* remove or damage the piece of black expanded foam plastic which is glued onto this back-plate – it is essential to the correct operation of the oscillator and *must* be replaced after the tuning modification is completed.
3. Drill out the earthing-screw hole and tap it 2BA, right through into the cavity.
4. Carefully remove all swarf from the cavity and then replace the back-plate.
5. Fit a 2BA PTFE screw into the newly tapped hole to provide smooth tuning.
6. With the tip of the PTFE screw flush with the inside face of the cavity, use the brass tuning screw to set the *highest* frequency to which the oscillator needs to tune and then lock it in place. Insertion of the PTFE screw will now tune the oscillator down in frequency by at least 300MHz.

Another Solfan module which has been widely used is also illustrated in Fig 10.14. This consists of an oscillator with a built-in in-line mixer with an offset mixer diode. An identical tuning modification can be made. The advantage of this type of oscillator is that the mixer diode current can be used to monitor the transmitter output and later can be used as a receive mixer. In other words, the unit is a ready-made wide-band 'transceiver' head which needs no transmit/receive switching.

The small module shown in Fig 10.15, made by AEI/Pascal, is another oscillator/mixer module which can sometimes be found on the surplus market. It is a very small unit, made from a solid block of aluminium. It can

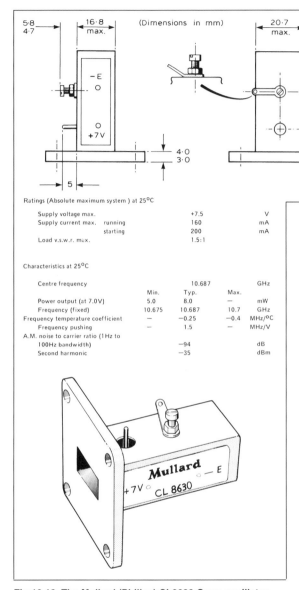

(Dimensions in mm)

Ratings (Absolute maximum system) at 25°C

Supply voltage max.	+7.5	V
Supply current max. running	160	mA
starting	200	mA
Load v.s.w.r. max.	1.5:1	

Characteristics at 25°C

	Min.	Typ.	Max.	
Centre frequency		10.687		GHz
Power output (at 7.0V)	5.0	8.0	—	mW
Frequency (fixed)	10.675	10.687	10.7	GHz
Frequency temperature coefficient	—	−0.25	−0.4	MHz/°C
Frequency pushing	—	1.5	—	MHz/V
A.M. noise to carrier ratio (1Hz to 100Hz bandwidth)		−94		dB
Second harmonic		−35		dBm

Fig 10.13. The Mullard (Philips) CL8630 Gunn oscillator

be used directly without any modification, needing only to be retuned to the amateur band. Again, the mixer diode can be used to monitor the transmitter output, or later as a receive mixer.

Setting the Gunn operating voltage
1. Connect a 12 to 13.5V supply to the input of the bias-supply/modulator unit.
2. Connect a meter to the output and set the Gunn voltage to about 7V.
3. Switch off, remove the meter and connect the bias

supply/modulator to the Gunn oscillator, positive output to the Gunn terminal and negative to the body of the oscillator, using a short length of miniature coaxial cable. Don't forget the anti-parasitic components on the Gunn terminal!

4. Switch on again. The oscillator should now be producing output which can be monitored by means of a multimeter (on, say, its 10mA range) connected to the mixer diode terminal if you are using one of the oscillator/mixer units. If not, you will have to buy or make a

Fig 10.14. Solfan (USA) Gunn modules. Left, oscillator/mixer. Right, oscillator only

Fig 10.15. AEI/Pascal Gunn oscillator/mixer

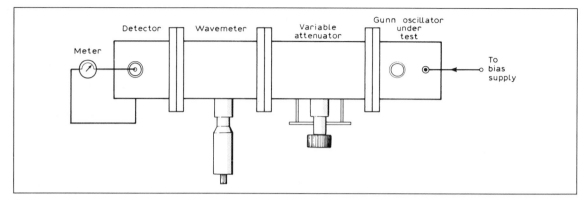

Fig 10.16. Waveguide test rig to measure Gunn operating voltages, output power and frequency

separate detector (see later) and use this to detect the oscillator output. The output frequency does not matter for this part of the alignment.

5. For best operation, set the Gunn voltage to about 0.5 to 1V above the 'starting voltage' – that is, the voltage at which oscillation reliably starts.

At this point the oscillator can be tuned smoothly over a wide range using either the metal tuning screw (for coarse tuning) or the PTFE screw (if fitted) for fine tuning. Noise sidebands will be quietest at this voltage. This will be important when the oscillator is used in a receiver with a low IF such as 10.7MHz. It is less important if the oscillator is used only as a transmitter. Slightly more power will be generated at higher voltages, but the oscillator will then generally be less well behaved, possibly with a tendency to break into spurious modes of oscillation and probably with a greater tendency to drift due to thermal effects because of the higher power dissipation.

The front-panel control used to fine tune the Gunn by frequency pushing should have a very restricted range, ideally no greater than ±1V, as in the design described. Adjustment beyond this, while still tuning the device, may bring the operating point to the non-linear part of the characteristic curve, so that the deviation will vary greatly as the bias voltage is increased. The optimum operating point should be set by the preset resistor and left at that point!

Setting the Gunn frequency and measuring its power output

The ideal way to do this needs some basic test equipment: a calibrated variable waveguide attenuator, a waveguide detector, a calibrated absorption wavemeter and an analogue multimeter. If you have these (or know someone who has and will help you), set up a test rig like that shown in Fig 10.16. With a test rig like this you can measure both frequency and power output as well as several other things.

With a good (high-Q) absorption wavemeter at 10GHz you should be able to measure the frequency to about 2MHz. One of the problems in making measurements when using free-running (Gunn) oscillators is that, unless there is isolation between the oscillator and the wavemeter/detector, the oscillator frequency will be pulled by the wavemeter and lead to false measurements.

The simplest set-up to ensure that measurements will be as accurate as possible is that shown in Fig 10.16. The test method is simple:

1. Set the attenuator to about 10dB, detune the wavemeter well away from the expected frequency and set the multimeter to the 10mA range.

2. Start the Gunn oscillator – if this has an output in the range 10 to 20mW, then 1 to 2mA current should be seen on the multimeter.

3. Increase the attenuation until, say, 25µA is seen on the meter and then switch the multimeter down to the 100µA range.

4. Increase attenuation again until a reading of, say, 10µA is obtained. This gives an isolation of 30 to 33dB (1000 to 2000 times down) between the oscillator and wavemeter.

5. Now tune the wavemeter *slowly* for a dip in the meter reading, read the wavemeter scale and record the frequency. Detune the wavemeter again.

6. If you are using a surplus Gunn oscillator, you will need to reset the frequency into the amateur band. This is done by loosening the locknut on the (metal) tuning screw *slightly* and turning the screw *slowly inwards*. Follow the frequency change with the wavemeter and keep adjusting the screw *slowly* until the frequency is where you want it. Tighten the locknut again and detune the wavemeter.

You can now measure the power output of your oscillator. Calibration graphs of power against detector current for both point-contact and Schottky diodes are given in Figs

10.17 and 10.18. Depending on the type of detector diode used, the current can be translated directly into power using one or other of the two graphs. Better indications of low power levels at the detector are given by using a point-contact diode (eg 1N23 type) for power measurement. You should note the current and translate the reading into power. You should also note the setting of the attenuator. If the indicated power is 0.01mW (current about 15μA for a point-contact diode working into a multimeter of resistance 1kΩ on the 100μA range) and the reading on the calibrated attenuator is 30dB, then the oscillator power output is 30dB (1000 times) up on 0.01mW, ie 10mW. The accuracy of the measurement will depend on the calibration curve for the diode but should be good enough for you to know, within a milliwatt or so, what power output your oscillator is giving.

At the same time as making these measurements you can make several other important measurements. By connecting a voltmeter to the output of the Gunn supply to measure the Gunn voltage, it is possible to measure the starting voltage, the power output at various bias voltages, the bias voltage for maximum power output and the maximum (turn-off) voltage. The optimum Gunn bias voltage for quietest operation can thus be measured. The output against Gunn voltage is shown in Fig 10.19. You can see that there is a 'turn-on' voltage at which oscillation starts, then a linear part of the curve where power output increases steadily with the applied voltage. The power curve becomes non-linear towards the maximum power output voltage and then

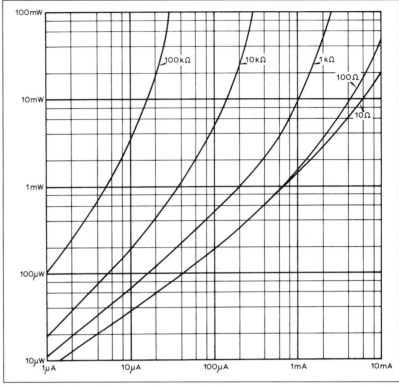

Fig 10.17. Diode current/power curves for a point-contact diode. Curves are given for various meter resistances

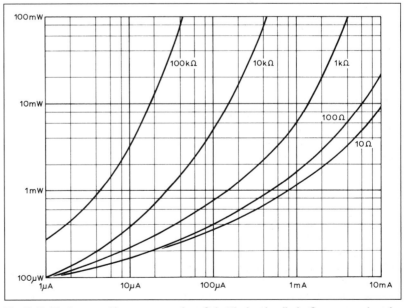

Fig 10.18. Diode current/power curves for a Schottky barrier diode. Curves are given for various meter resistances

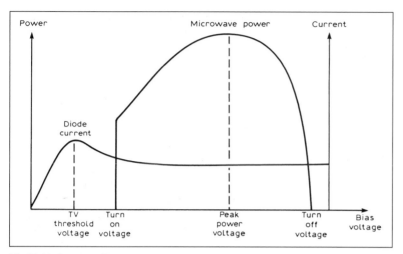

Fig 10.19. Gunn oscillator power output plotted against Gunn voltage

falls again to a point where there is 'turn-off' and the Gunn stops oscillating. Gunn oscillators should never be operated near either the turn-on or turn-off voltages as they will dissipate more power and may burn out. The best point is in the middle of the most linear part of the curve.

Measurements of frequency at each of the voltage settings will let you measure the 'voltage-pushing' factor of the Gunn, along with an estimate of the optimum voltage-pushing range to be set by the FINE TUNE potentiometer on the Gunn supply. It is sometimes possible that the Gunn tuning is not as smooth as expected: it may jump in frequency by some tens of megahertz and then continue tuning normally, due to the oscillator changing modes. This may be very hard to detect as the power output may not change much. These jumps can be the cause of unexplained inability to hear another station when the oscillator is used in a receiver – the oscillator may jump past the other station's frequency! The best way to check for such effects is to tune the Gunn across its frequency range with its tuning screw while following it continuously with the wavemeter and watching for sudden jumps. This process should be repeated at several different Gunn bias voltages within its electrical tuning range. If the Gunn oscillator is used as a fixed-frequency transmitter only, then you don't really need to make these measurements.

If you don't have the components to make a test rig or access to a test rig, then it is still possible to set the frequency but much less accurately. Fig 10.20 shows how this can be done when using an oscillator/mixer unit. With an oscillator-only unit, the unit should be fixed at one end of the scale and a separate detector (with a small horn antenna) moved along the scale instead of the fixed metal sheet. With care and several measurements made

with the greatest possible separation between the Gunn unit and either the metal plate or the separate detector, the frequency can probably be set to about 20MHz.

Narrow-band sources for 10GHz

Narrow-band (NB) signals at 10GHz are usually generated by multiplication from a lower frequency in several steps. Multiplication generates harmonics other than the wanted frequency and filtering of the output is essential. Narrow-band equipment is much more complicated than the simple wide-band sources described so far and is more difficult to make. This should not deter determined amateurs! Another requirement for successful construction of narrow-band equipment is test gear for alignment. The best way of approaching the problems of constructing and operating NB equipment is first to get experience of 10GHz

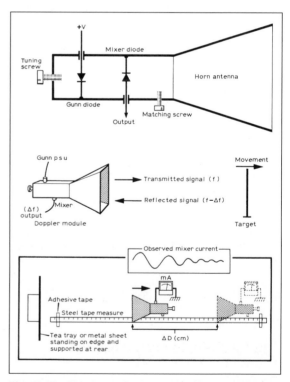

Fig 10.20. Simple method of approximate frequency measurement (see text) when you have no other means at your disposal!

techniques by building and operating WB equipment and then go on to NB techniques once you feel confident enough. One thing is for certain – most, if not all, of the waveguide components used for WB will be of equal use later. There is always a use for 'wide-band' waveguide components! Many can be used as essential test equipment for NB.

At present, generating NB signals at 10GHz is fairly standard: a high-stability, low-noise source is multiplied in several stages to the final frequency. It is well filtered at each stage to remove the unwanted products of the multiplication process. Once the final frequency is reached, the signal may be amplified up to whatever power is needed from the transmitter. The gallium arsenide field-effect transistors (GaAsFETs) needed to get powers above about 100mW are still very expensive, so we will consider power output between about 50 and 100mW only.

A narrow-band 10GHz transmitter

The frequency source should always start at the highest practicable frequency. This will maximise harmonic spacing and minimise the multiplication factor. Wide harmonic spacing makes filtering easier and minimum multiplication gives higher efficiency. The starting frequency, for the reasons given earlier, will be somewhere in the region of 100MHz. Again, a good, stable and noise-free oscillator must be used. As at 1.3GHz, the simplest modulation modes are either CW (FSK or AFSK) or NBFM.

The transmitter to be described is built in two units. The first, designed by Sam Jewell, G4DDK, is a crystal oscillator source with filtered output at around 2.5GHz (G4DDK-004). This unit is similar to the G4DDK-001 unit described as a 1.3GHz transmitter earlier. It uses mainly 'ordinary' components on a specially produced glassfibre PCB which is available from the RSGB Microwave Committee Components Service. Once again, don't try to make your own board – it may not work!

The second unit, designed by Charles Suckling, G3WDG, is a ×4 multiplier and amplifier unit which uses mainly SMD components and is built on a specially produced PTFE PCB. The GaAsFETs used are 'surplus' types. This design is described in less detail than the first unit because the methods used are so different that a booklet is supplied with the PCB and special components as part of a 'mini-kit', should you decide you want to build it.

The G4DDK-004 crystal oscillator source for 2.0 to 2.6GHz

The G4DDK-004 oscillator source is a direct development of the G4DDK-001 unit described earlier but has an extra multiplier stage to provide output in the 2 to 2.6GHz frequency range. This frequency range can be used as a local oscillator in receive and transmit converters for the 2.3GHz amateur band. It can also be used as a low-power personal beacon or control transmitter operating in the same band under the terms of the UK licence. Modern 10GHz narrow-band transverters need local oscillator drive at 2556MHz. This was the original reason for developing the unit. Versions of this unit have been built with outputs in the range 2176MHz to 2556MHz and the unit should be usable with outputs between 2.0 and 2.6GHz.

Circuit description

The circuit of the source is shown in Fig 10.21. Component values are given in Table 10.3. The crystal oscillator is the Butler circuit used in the G4DDK-001 design. In that design, it was mentioned that it might be necessary to put a small-value capacitor in series with the crystal if the oscillator would not restart properly after pulling onto frequency. In this design, there are solder pads for such a capacitor. If it is not required, then a *short* wire link should bridge the Cx pads or a ceramic 1nF capacitor should be used. The source may be narrowband frequency modulated using the circuit in Fig 9.14 (Chapter 9).

SKY (green) trimmers were used for C13 and C14 because they were available. Any small (5mm diameter) 5pF trimmer could be used but, since you must use green SKY trimmers in the output filter, it makes sense to use them here as well. Similarly, SKY trimmers can be used for C18, 19, and 20, although the black Murata type could be used in this stage depending on required frequency. The final multiplier originally used a BFG91A and operated well at these frequencies, easily achieving the specified output. This type of transistor has two emitter connections and both must be thoroughly decoupled to ground to ensure stable operation; however, only one emitter has DC connection to ground through R19. During later development, it was found that a BFR91A (with a single emitter connection) could replace the BFG91A which was sometimes unstable. With the BFR91A, two extra decoupling capacitors are needed (see later) and one of the emitter tracks is unused, although still on the board. Additional decoupling has been provided in the collector supply circuit of this stage using a quarter-wave, open-circuit, low-impedance transmission line. The open-circuit at the end of the line is transformed to a short-circuit quarter-wave away at the junction of R20 and the quarter-wave choke line formed by the track from C29 to R20. Although this arrangement can only be optimum at one frequency, in practice the bandwidth of the line is such that it still remains effective over the entire range 2.0 to 2.6GHz.

This design does not use the collector supply chokes

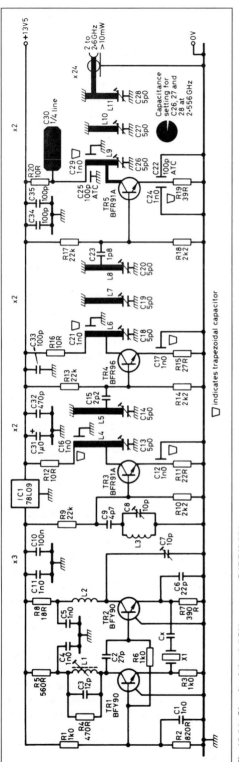

Fig 10.21. Circuit of the 2.5GHz source G4DDK-004

Table 10.3. Components list for the G4DDK-004 2.5GHz oscillator source

RESISTORS

R1, 3, 6	1k0
R2	820R
R4	470R
R5	560R
R7	390R
R8	18R
R9, 13, 17	22k
R10,14, 18	2k2
R11	22R
R12, 16, 20	10R
R15	27R
R19	39R

Resistors are 0.25W miniature carbon film or metal film.

CAPACITORS

C1, 4, 5, 11	1000p high-K ceramic plate, eg Philips 629 series
C2	27p low-K ceramic plate, eg Philips 632 series
C3	12p low-K ceramic plate, eg Philips 632 series
C6	22p low-K ceramic plate, eg Philips 632 series
C9	4p7 low-K ceramic plate, eg Philips 632 series
C15	2p2 low-K ceramic plate, eg Philips 632 series
C23	1p8 low-K ceramic plate, eg Philips 632 series
C31, 32, 33	470p medium-K ceramic plate, eg Philips 630 series
C22, 34, 35	100p low-K ceramic plate, eg Philips 632 series
C10	0.1µ tantalum bead, 16V working
C12, 16, 17	1n trapezoidal (RSGB or Cirkit)
C21, 24	470p trapezoidal (RSGB or Cirkit)
C25, 29	22p trapezoidal (RSGB or Cirkit)
C7, 8	10p miniature trimmer (5mm diameter), eg Cirkit 06-10008
C13, 14, 18, 19, 20, 26, 27, 28	SKY trimmer (green) (Piper Communications)
C30	PCB track
Cx	10 to 33p, type as C3 (see text)

INDUCTORS

L1	Toko S18 5.5 turns (green) with aluminium core
L2, 3	2 turns of 1mm diameter tinned copper wire, inside diameter 4mm. Turns spaced to fit hole spacing. Exceptionally 3 turns at low-frequency end of range.
L4 to 11	Printed on PCB

SEMICONDUCTORS

TR1, 2	BFY90
TR3	BFR91A
TR4	BFR96
TR5	BFG91A (Piper)
IC1	78L09

MISCELLANEOUS

X1   Fifth overtone crystal in HC18/U case. Frequency of crystal = $F_{out}/24$

Tin-plate box, type 45 (7768) Piper Communications. 55.5mm wide by 148mm long by 30mm high.
Output socket, single-hole SMA, SMB or SMC

used in the 1152MHz unit. These chokes have caused problems in the past due to difficulty in obtaining the required axial lead types. The 10Ω resistors are not as effective as chokes but the decoupling capacitor values have been carefully chosen to be as effective as possible

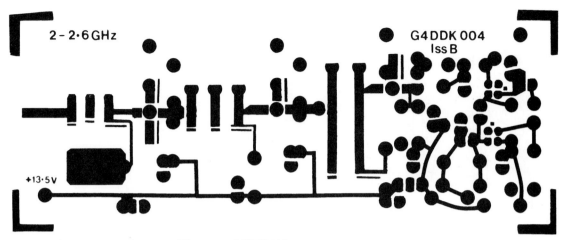

Fig 10.22. PCB track layout for the 2.5GHz source G4DDK-004

in the frequency ranges encountered in their respective stages.

Construction

The unit is designed to fit into the type 45 tinplate box (also known as type 7768). This box is 55.5 × 148 × 30mm and retails at low cost compared with die-cast boxes of similar size.

A full-size PCB layout has been provided for the oscillator unit (Fig 10.22), together with a component overlay (Fig 10.23). A high-quality PCB (G4DDK-004) is available, ready drilled, slotted and tinned from the Microwave Committee Components Service.

1. File small areas of board to clear the two overlapping corners of the tin plate box.
2. Place the board inside the 'L' shaped half of the tin plate box. The box should not be soldered together at this stage.
3. Fit L1 into its mounting holes, but do not solder it in place.
4. Position the board so that the top of L1 is 5mm below the rim of the box, and mark all round the inside of the box where the board will be soldered into place.
5. Transfer the line to the inside of the other half of the box, and mark where the output socket is to be mounted. The hole must be placed to allow the spill of the connector to lie flush with the output track on the PCB. It is better to use a panel-mounting socket and solder it flush to the outside wall of the box with its spill protruding into the box. The socket should be an SMA, SMB, or SMC (CONHEX) type. N-types are too large and BNC connectors can be unreliable at these frequencies.
6. Drill the socket mounting hole.
7. Drill a hole in the same end of the box to take the feedthrough capacitor that will be used to bring DC power into the box.
8. If a crystal heater is to be used, then drill a hole for the power feedthrough for this in the other end wall of the box.
9. Drill holes for feedthrough capacitors needed for the modulation input and keying. The value of the modulation input capacitor should not be more than 1000pF.
10. Carefully spot-solder the board into one half of the tin box.
11. Spot-solder the other half of the box into place, ensuring a good fit. It may be necessary to carefully file a small amount of the PCB away at the ends or sides to get a comfortable fit.
12. Once you are sure that the board fits well and is in the right position, solder along the whole of the sides and ends of the box to give a good RF-tight connection.
13. The box corners can now be soldered.
14. Cut five short lengths of thin copper strip and solder them at the ends of L5, 7, 8, 10 and 11, as shown in the component overlay diagram Fig 10.23.
15. Solder all the resistors and capacitors (with the shortest possible leads) into place where shown, taking care to solder grounded leads both top and bottom of the board.
16. Solder the coils into place, remembering to solder the grounded end of L3 both top and bottom.
17. Solder TR1 and TR2 into place, making sure they are seated well down onto the board but leaving just enough room to solder the case lead of both transistors to the ground plane of the board.
18. Solder IC1 into place, remembering to ground the centre lead.

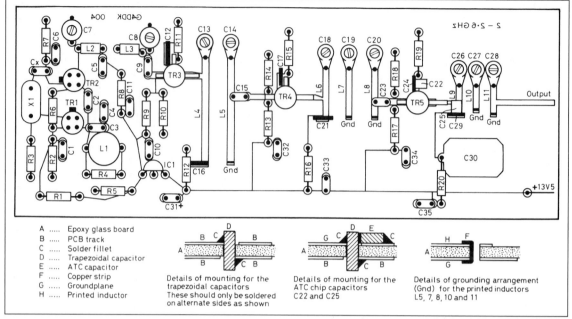

A ..... Epoxy glass board
B ..... PCB track
C ..... Solder fillet
D ..... Trapezoidal capacitor
E ..... ATC capacitor
F ..... Copper strip
G ..... Groundplane
H ..... Printed inductor

Details of mounting for the
trapezoidal capacitors
These should only be soldered
on alternate sides as shown

Details of mounting for the
ATC chip capacitors
C22 and C25

Details of grounding arrangement
(Gnd) for the printed inductors
L5, 7, 8, 10 and 11

Fig 10.23. (a) Component layout for the 2.5GHz source G4DDK-004. (b) Photo of completed G4DDK-004 (G3PFR)

19. Solder the trapezoidal capacitors into place as shown in the component overlay diagram.
20. Carefully bend the flat connection lead of the SKY trimmers out at 90° to the capacitor body.
21. Place the trimmer with the round lead in the hole in the tuned line.
22. Solder the trimmer to the tuned line, then solder the flat lead to the ground plane.
23. C7 and C8 can be treated in the same way but, unless black SKY trimmers are being used, the mounting arrangement may be different. Use the shortest possible leads on the trimmers, whichever type you choose to use.
24. Solder TR3, 4 and 5 into place, taking care to get the leads the right way round. Solder the crystal into place last, seating it well down onto the board. You may need to earth the case of the crystal, especially if a heater is to be used.

Alignment

In this section it is assumed that the unit is to be aligned to 2592MHz (this will later give output at 10,368MHz in the 10GHz band). It is possible to align the oscillator/multiplier with nothing more than a multimeter. However, this won't tell you what frequency the unit is tuned to, or what output level has been achieved. As far as aligning the unit is concerned, the most essential items of test equipment are a *moving-coil* (analogue) multimeter and

absorption wavemeter(s) to cover the range 106 to 2600MHz. A digital multimeter is not suitable for tuning-up as it can give *very* misleading results. The wavemeter is also preferable to a frequency counter since it not only indicates the required output but also the presence of any unwanted signals.

1. Connect a 13.5V supply and check that the unit takes no more than about 150mA. If the current is much higher than this, switch off and check for faults.
2. When all is well, check that the regulated voltage from IC1 is 9V.
3. Place the wavemeter pick-up coil close to L1 and tune to 108MHz, then adjust the core of L1 for a strong reading.
4. Switch off then on and check that the oscillator restarts. If not, adjust L1 core a quarter-turn and try again. The exact frequency does not matter at this stage.
5. Set the multimeter to its 2.5V range (or nearest equivalent) and connect across R11, then slowly adjust C7 then C8 for a maximum reading. When you

adjust C7 initially you may only see the slightest movement of the meter. This is normal and what you are looking for. A digital meter will probably miss it due to the up-dating method used.

6. Peak the reading with C8.
7. Confirm with the wavemeter that you have set L2 and L3 to the required third harmonic of the crystal frequency at 324MHz.
8. Transfer the meter to R15 and adjust C13 and C14 for a maximum voltage reading across R15.
9. Confirm that you have selected the correct harmonic at 648MHz.
10. Transfer the meter to R19 and adjust C18, 19 and 20 for a maximum reading. Because there are three tuned circuits this time, the initial meter movement may be very small. The middle tuned circuit tunes especially sharply.
11. Confirm with the wavemeter that you have tuned these circuits to 1296MHz. You could also listen for the correct harmonic on a 23cm receiver if one is available.
12. Connect an absorption wavemeter, preferably the type with built-in diode detector described in the 1.3GHz section, to the output connector, and tune the wavemeter to 2592MHz.
13. Adjust C26, 27 and 28 to obtain a maximum reading. This should be close to 10mW if your wavemeter is also calibrated for output power. As mentioned earlier, use an insulated trimming tool to adjust the output trimmers. Any metal-bladed trimming tool will affect the tuning point and may well prevent the circuits resonating as high as 2592MHz.
14. It is now worth going back over the previous adjustments and re-peaking to obtain maximum output. If any adjustment requires more than the slightest tweak, be suspicious of the alignment of that stage! In these circumstances it is often worth starting alignment from the beginning again.

If the output frequency is a little low and pulling it up onto frequency results in reduced output or failure to restart after switching off and then back on, it may be necessary to add the capacitor Cx as previously mentioned. This should cure the problem. If not, change the crystal!

Due to component tolerances, there was some instability in the final multiplier stage, making the unit difficult to align: the remedy for this is to replace the BFG91A with a BFR91A and to add, on the upper surface of the board, additional decoupling in the form of two 100pF ceramic chip capacitors soldered across C17 and C24. It is possible, with a little care, to fit these extra capacitors between the ground plane and the silvering of the existing trapezoidal capacitor, making modification to the board unnecessary. These are shown on the layout diagram. It has sometimes been found necessary to shorten the centre line of the output filter by 1 to 1.5mm, especially if operation towards the high end of the range is needed (as here). This can be done either by soldering a 1mm PCB pin through a hole drilled in the ground plane and line or by cutting another narrow slot at the right point and using copper foil in the usual manner. These modifications have often resulted in an output of between +11 and +13dBm. To realise highest power output it has also been found essential to use type BFR91A transistors, not the older BFR91.

One unexpected use for the board has emerged since the prototypes were built. The tuning range of the final multiplier filter is such that it will tune as low as 1.2GHz, allowing the final multiplier to operate as an amplifier producing 50 to 70mW output. In this form, the board may be used as a low-power transmitter in the 1.3GHz band!

The G3WDG-001 multiplier/amplifier for 10.0 to 10.5GHz

The construction of this design using PCBs, SMD components and GaAsFETs follows lower-frequency practice rather than 'waveguide plumbing', although care and attention to detail are still needed if good results are to be obtained. Until now, the cost of construction has been too high for many amateurs, especially beginners.

Recently a large quantity of GaAsFETs became available on the surplus market in the UK at a fraction of the cost of 'new' devices. The GaAsFETs were manufactured by the Plessey 3-5 Group for use in 11GHz satellite TV LNBs and have excellent performance. The low cost of these led the to development of this design (and other designs not described here).

The G3WDG-001 design is a ×4 multiplier/amplifier transmitter chain which can provide 50 to 100mW output anywhere in the 10.0 to 10.5GHz band. It can be used as a simple CW/FM narrow-band transmitter, a beacon or personal signal source, as an ATV transmitter or as a packet radio link transmitter.

This design is intended for home construction without either very difficult construction methods or elaborate test equipment. Wherever possible low-cost components have been used, but in some cases it has been necessary to use more expensive components. The specified parts *must* be used or the design will not work properly.

All the specialised components, with the exception of the GaAsFETs, are available as a 'mini-kit' from the Microwave Committee Components Service. The GaAsFETs are available from one of the suppliers in Appendix 2.

It is a good idea, for those who have not built microwave PCB designs before, to build a simple design like this before trying something more complicated such as a receiver or transverter. Many of the construction techniques are not described in detail here as they are given in full detail in the construction booklet which is part of the 'mini-kit'.

The design requires drive input of 10mW or more in the 2.5 to 2.6GHz region for full output at 10GHz. The exact frequency depends on the particular application. This drive can be obtained from the G4DDK-004 unit just described.

The design is built on special PTFE-glass board and, in the main, surface-mount 'chip' devices (SMDs) are used, although some more familiar 'ordinary' components are also used. GaAsFETs are used as an active multiplier and amplifiers. Microstrip lines are used to give the correct operating impedances for the GaAsFETs and the circuit has been designed to cover the whole of the 10GHz band from 10.0 to 10.5GHz. A reliable method for grounding the source leads of the GaAsFETs was developed to ensure that the designs would be reproducible – this uses small PCB pins.

High selectivity required to discriminate between harmonics is provided by the use of a small 'pill-box' tuned cavity resonator soldered to the board. Coupling from the microstrip lines into and out of the resonator is by using probes. A high drive oscillator frequency has been chosen (around 2.5GHz), to make filtering easier. The drive from the G4DDK-004 unit is very clean and this also makes filtering easier. Each GaAsFET amplifier stage provides a gain of about 10dB. Matched input and output circuits use microstrip lines. Rather than try to etch very narrow (high-impedance) microstrip lines, where these are necessary, it is easier to use short lengths of thin wire soldered to the lines and pads on the surface of the board.

The PCB available from the Microwave Committee Components Service as part of the 'mini-kit' should be used for this design. Both the board material and the dimensions of the microstrip lines are critical. The other critical components, such as the ceramic chip capacitors, resistors and the silver-plated resonators, are supplied in the kit. A regulator board and comprehensive instruction booklet are also included. Virtually all the other components are available from easily accessible amateur sources.

Only the recommended, first-grade known components should be used – substitution from the 'junk-box' or components 'salvaged' from other microwave equipment is just not good enough! The recommended 'surplus' GaAsFETs are perfectly good for this design.

The PCB should be soldered into a tin-plate box (or an alternative, specially made brass or copper enclosure of similar size and form). By doing this, the rather flexible board is housed rigidly and also well screened and

thermally insulated to some degree. The finished, boxed units (both the drive unit and this unit) should be housed in a rigid outer box to provide even better mechanical and thermal stability. This 'boxes within boxes' approach is essential for high-performance microwave equipment.

SMA connectors should be used for input and output. N-type connectors are too big, and other types do not work at these frequencies. The 12V power supply (or any other ingoing supplies) must be well decoupled by 1nF to 10nF solder-in feedthrough capacitors or Filtercons. The power supplies must be stabilised to the voltages given in the circuit diagram: if these voltages are exceeded, or the gate bias (negative) voltage fails, the GaAsFETs can be damaged, if not destroyed. By including resistors in the drain circuits there is some current-limiting protection. It is well worth spending time on this part of the circuit, using only generously rated and reliable components.

Care and attention to detail is essential *and* your soldering techniques must be good! Components should be mounted in the order given and the GaAsFET devices should always be the last components to be soldered into place, taking the precautions mentioned earlier: that is, grounding together the constructor, the body of the soldering iron and the case/ground plane of the PCB while soldering them in place. In this way the risk of damage by static is avoided.

The circuit is shown in Fig 10.24, the layout of the board and components in Fig 10.25 and their values in Table 10.4.

Drive at 2592MHz (for output at 10,368MHz) is required at a level of 10mW or greater. This is supplied by the G4DDK-004 oscillator multiplier strip, the crystal being a fifth overtone HC18/U type around 108MHz. You can calculate the crystal frequency by taking the 10GHz frequency and dividing by 96. For example, 10,368MHz/96 = 108.0000MHz, 10,368.5MHz/96 = 108.0052MHz, and so on.

Because of component tolerances and differences in the accuracy of construction and alignment, varying levels of output are obtained from the G4DDK-004 source. To be sure that enough drive is present, a broad-band microwave monolithic integrated circuit (MMIC) amplifier, using an Avantek MSA0504 device, is used as the input stage. This will provide plenty of gain to drive the GaAsFET multiplier, F1 (Fig 10.25), at the input frequency. There is a gap in the input microstrip which is large enough to take the body of the MMIC. A 3.7mm hole must be *carefully* drilled in the middle of this gap, before any other construction starts, so that the MMIC can be mounted in the board with minimum lead length – in a manner similar to the BFR91/6 transistor package used in the driver board G4DDK-004.

The output from the MMIC is matched to the input

impedance of the multiplier FET by a 'lumped element' network consisting of L2/L3. L3 is also used to feed the negative gate bias to the FET from RV1, which sets the optimum operating bias for the multiplier. The output circuit at the drain of the FET consists of a series resonant circuit at 2.5GHz followed by some microstrip matching elements at 10GHz. A series-

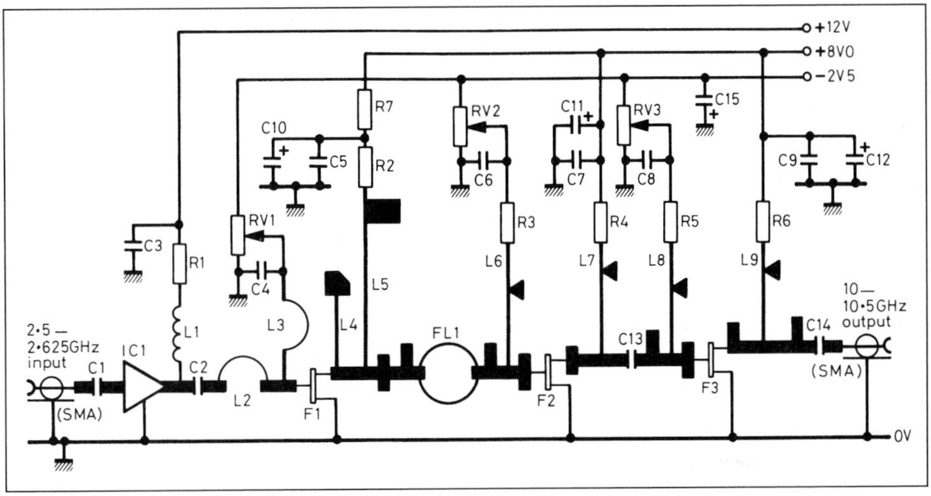

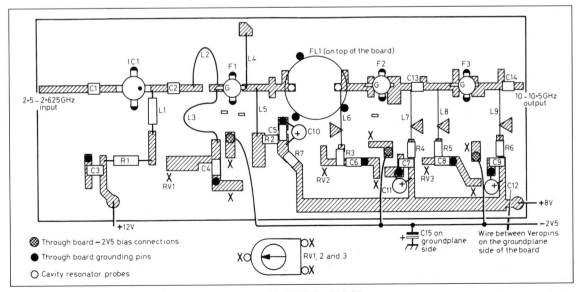

Fig 10.24. Circuit of the G3WDG-001 multiplier/amplifier. This unit multiplies the 2.5GHz output of the G4DDK-004 source into the 10GHz band, filters it to remove unwanted harmonics and then amplifies the 10GHz signal to at least 50mW output

resonant circuit is formed by L4 and a printed capacitor (identified by the cut corner). The function of this circuit is to 'short-circuit' the input frequency to ground, which improves multiplier efficiency considerably. The drain bias circuit consists of a quarter-wave choke, L5, connected to a quarter-wave stub. The tip of the stub is at very low impedance at its resonant frequency (10GHz). This is transformed by L5 to a very high impedance. In this way there is virtually no disturbance to the signals on the microstrip line from the bias network. This type of bias network is fine at its operating frequency but needs

additional decoupling at lower frequencies. This is accomplished primarily by R2 and C5 which load the drain of the FET resistively at low frequencies, giving broad-band stability. C10 is used for further decoupling at very low frequencies. This bias configuration is used in other G3WDG 10GHz designs (not described here), except that in many locations the quarter-wave stub is replaced by a triangular element, known as a 'radial stub'. This has the same properties as a stub (the tip of the element is at very low impedance) but is very much smaller, resulting in a more compact layout.

Fig 10.25. Layout of the surface mount components on the G3WDG-001 PCB

Table 10.4. Components list for the G3WDG-001 2.5GHz to 10GHz multiplier/amplifier

RESISTORS

R1	39R ¼W carbon film
R2–6	47R SMD, 0805 size
R7	220R (may need to be adjusted on test) SMD, size 0805. Alternatively, use a wire-ended ¼W carbon or metal film resistor, stood on end.
RV1, 2, 3	2k2 miniature horizontal preset with legs bent out at 90° and cut to fit board. These are fitted after all other parts except the GaAsFETs. This is necessary due to other parts being located below them. Connect to the points marked 'X' on the layout diagram. No tracking is provided between the bias connection points. This should be done with fine, insulated wire.

CAPACITORS

C1 to C9	220pF SMD, 0805 size
C10, 11, 12	10µ tantalum bead or miniature electrolytic, 10V wkg
C13, 14	2.2p ATC chip capacitor, series 100 or 130

INDUCTORS

L1	8 turns of 0.315mm diameter enamelled copper wire (ECW) close wound and self-supporting
L2	16mm length of 0.315mm diameter ECW formed into a hairpin shape and laid flat on the board. 1mm at each end used for soldered termination
L3	As L2, but 19.5mm long
L4, 5	Straight length of 0.315mm ECW between stub and track
L6–9	Straight length of 0.2mm silver or tinned copper wire between radial stub and track. A single strand of braid from a scrap length of RG214 cable is suitable. Mount flat to PCB.

SEMICONDUCTORS

F1, 2, 3	P35-1108 GaAsFET (Birkett BLACK spot)

MISCELLANEOUS

FL1	Brass cavity resonator. Silver plated. Tuning by means of a silver plated M4 screw with lock-nut. Two probes each 4.7mm overall length as shown

PCB pins, RS Components 433-864, 1mm dia, 1.5mm head dia (approx)

Two SMA sockets

Tin-plate box type 7754 (37 × 111 × 30mm) from Piper Communications.

Solder feedthrough capacitors, 1nF to 10nF or Filtercons

Positive and negative regulated supplies, eg positive from 7808 IC, negative from ICL7660 voltage converter, see diagrams

---

R7 is used to set the drain voltage to an optimum value for best multiplier performance.

The output from the multiplier consists of several harmonics, but mainly the wanted fourth harmonic of the drive frequency. This is fed into FL1, the resonator filter, by means of a probe. Filtered output is coupled to the gate of the first amplifier, F2, by means of a second probe. The resonator is tuned by means of an M4 screw, locked in place with a lock-nut after tuning to resonance. The resonator body and tuning screw should be silver plated.

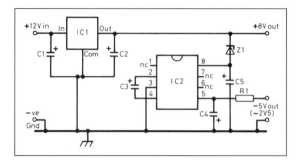

Fig 10.26. Positive and negative voltage regulator circuits for the G3WDG-001 module (G4FRE). Component values: IC1, µA7808; IC2, ICL7660PCA; Z1, 3.0V or 3.3V, 400mW zener diode; R1 3.3kΩ ¼W metal film; C1, 1µF tantalum bead, 16V working; C2, 0.1µF tantalum bead, 10V working; C3, C4, 22µF tantalum bead, 10V working; C5, 10µF tantalum bead, 10V working; PCB, G4FRE-023

Not only does this increase the Q of the cavity, but also makes the cavity much easier to solder to the board. GaAsFETs F2 and F3 form a cascaded two-stage amplifier giving about 20dB gain, each with gate and drain bias arrangements similar to those of the multiplier stage. DC blocking and RF coupling in the drain circuits is accomplished by means of 2.2pF chip capacitors which *must* be designed specifically for such frequencies, for example ATC series 100 or 130. The ordinary chip capacitors used for lower-frequency coupling or decoupling are definitely not suitable in these two positions.

The drain supply of the three GaAsFET stages must not exceed 8V measured at the supply rail, otherwise their ratings may be exceeded and they will become expensive, fast-acting fuses! A gate bias rail at −2.5V is needed to set their operating points. Two simple IC regulator circuits are built onto a small glassfibre board fixed in the ground plane compartment of the box. The regulator circuit is shown in Fig 10.26 and layout for the regulator is shown in Fig 10.27. Note that the PCB layout shown for the regulator board requires the components to be mounted on the track side, as if the components were surface-mount devices.

Construction

The procedures, order of construction and special methods are fully described in the construction booklet and must be followed exactly! They are so well described that they will not be detailed here. In outline, the order of construction is:

1. Prepare, mark and drill the box.
2. Fit all the grounding pins.
3. Fit the resonator.
4. Mount the board in its box.
5. Fit input and output sockets.
6. Fit feedthroughs.

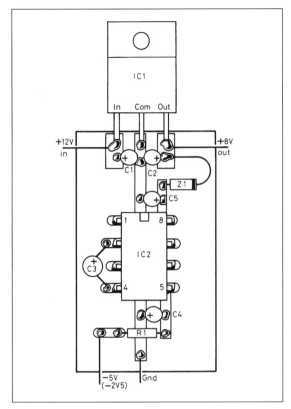

Fig 10.27. Layout of the regulator circuit on the G4FRE PCB. Although ordinary components are used, they are all surface mounted

7. Fit the inductors.

8. Fit the resistors and capacitors.

9. Fit the regulator circuit and test that both the +8V and −2.5V voltages are present and correct on the respective tracks/pins.

10. On completion of this test, disconnect power and solder in the devices (MMIC and GaAsFETs) *only if everything checks out correctly.*

Alignment with simple test gear

Once completed, the PCB should be carefully examined for poor joints, accidental solder bridges and other forms of short-circuit. Once satisfied that all is well, the alignment procedure may begin. You should already have checked before mounting the IC and FETs that the correct supply voltages will appear on the positive and negative supply rails when a +12 to +13.5V supply is connected to the input feedthrough capacitor.

1. Turn the bias potentiometers RV1, RV2 and RV3 fully clockwise so that full (cut-off) bias will be applied to the gates of the three GaAsFETs when power is applied.

2. Insert a multimeter in series with the +8V supply between the regulator output and the +8V rail and set it to, say, 500mA full-scale deflection.

3. Attach a suitable load/power indicator to the output socket. This might consist of an SMA to waveguide-16 transition, variable attenuator, wavemeter and detector connected as shown in Fig 10.16. Here's where some of your older WG components come into their own again!

4. With no oscillator drive applied to the input socket, apply +12V to the power input feedthrough. Current consumption should be no more than a few micro-amps of 'leakage' current. Switch the range of the multimeter as needed. If considerably more current is measured, look for short-circuits or wrongly connected or damaged components.

5. If all is well, adjust RV1 so that the current consumption rises to about 2 or 3mA.

6. Adjust RV2 for a further rise of 20mA in total current.

7. Repeat for RV3, again looking for a rise in current of a further 20mA. At this stage the current consumption should be of the order of 42 to 45mA.

8. Set the variable attenuator in the load/power indicator to minimum and detune the wavemeter well away from the expected frequency.

9. Apply drive to the input socket at a level of 10mW or more. Some output may be seen on the power detector meter and the current consumption may rise slightly.

10. Starting with the tuning screw just entering the cavity, slowly adjust the filter tuning screw inwards until the output begins to rise.

11. Continue adjusting for rising power output while increasing the attenuation to prevent excess current in the detector diode.

12. When adjusted for maximum output, check that the correct harmonic has been selected by using the wavemeter. The tuning range of the cavity is such that at least two, and probably three, harmonics of the 2.5GHz drive frequency can be peaked by the tuning screw – hence the need to check that the right harmonic has been chosen. Continue adjusting the tuning screw until you are certain that the correct harmonic has been selected and peaked. Lock the screw in position with the locknut.

13. Adjust the gate bias settings slightly to optimise output, starting with the multiplier FET (F1) and finishing with the output FET (F3).

14. Readjust and lock the cavity tuning screw as necessary.

There is some spread of characteristics of the completed units, so the bias current settings given in steps 5, 6 and 7 above should be regarded as starting figures only.

However, no stage should be allowed to pass more than about 50mA and the output stage should always work into a well-matched load. Some current-limiting protection is afforded by the 47Ω resistors in the drain feeds.

This completes the alignment: the power output should lie between a minimum of 50mW and a maximum of 100mW. It is not advisable to try to squeeze more power output than this, especially if the load is not too well matched although, if you can guarantee a good match, more output can be obtained by changing R6 for a 10Ω resistor. However, this is rather 'caning' the final amplifier and excess dissipation in any stage may lead to rapid destruction of the device concerned. You have been warned!

Modulation and stability

The frequency stability of the drive source oscillator is very, very important since the crystal frequency is being multiplied by a total factor of 96. The drive source G4DDK-004 was evolved with this purpose in mind and, with a good-quality crystal (10ppm or better), housed as suggested, it will be found to give good stability at the 10GHz output frequency. However, stability can be improved still further by fitting a crystal heater, such as the Murata 'Posistor' type PTH507B01BM500N016 which simply clips onto the crystal casing, is supplied with 13.5V nominal and, after a short warm-up, maintains a steady crystal temperature regardless of ambient conditions. The initial in-rush (switch-on) current for a 'cold' heater is of the order of 0.5A but requires only 25mA maintenance current once at operating temperature.

Simple test equipment for the 10GHz band

Many pieces of 10GHz waveguide equipment are available as 'surplus'. These are often difficult or impossible to make at home. Only a brief description of some of them is given here, so that you know what to look out for. Some coaxial components, suitable for use at 10GHz, are also available and illustrated where appropriate.

Waveguide diode mounts – mixers/detectors

Mixers and detectors can be constructed in many ways. The construction of the mixer or detector is determined by the outline of the diode to be used. Low-powered Gunn diodes use the same package shown in Fig 10.28(a), known as 'SOD31 outline'. The most familiar package is the DO-22/SOD-47, illustrated in Fig 10.28(b), which is used for the 1N23 type point-contact diode and for some of the recent Schottky barrier diodes such as the BAV92 series. Older types had a fixed anode connector (collet) while more modern versions, such as the 1N415 series, are supplied with a removable collet which will fit either

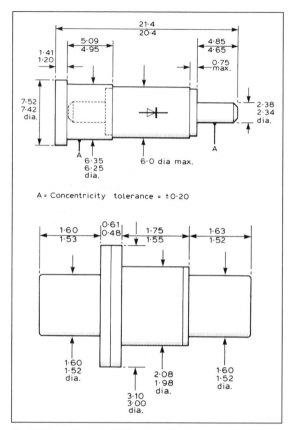

Fig 10.28. (a) Typical 10GHz mixer/detector diode package: this outline is used for 1N23-type point-contact diodes and some more recent Schottky barrier diodes. It is designed to fit inside the narrow measurement of WG16. It is known as the 'DO-22' or 'SOD-47' outline. (b) This package, known as the 'SOD31' outline, is used for low-power Gunn diodes, as well as mixer/detector diodes. In the case of low power Gunns, the flanged end is NEGATIVE and the other end is POSITIVE and is the heatsink end

the anode or cathode spigot of the device. This package is designed to fit within the narrow dimension of WG16. Most surplus WG16 diode mounts are suitable for amateur use. Often no modification is needed as they are broad-band and they can be used directly. It is sometimes possible to add a three-screw tuner immediately in front of the diode mount and so 'tune' the detector/mixer to amateur frequencies. Some typical surplus 10GHz waveguide mixers and detectors are shown in Fig 10.29.

A simple WG16 detector for 10GHz

The design of a simple detector is shown in Fig 10.30 and consists of a 1N23 type diode mounted centrally across the waveguide. The 'live' end of the diode is decoupled by the small capacitor formed between the end of the diode package and the inside wall of the

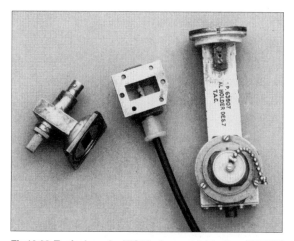

Fig 10.29. Typical surplus WG16 mixers and detectors *(G3PFR)*

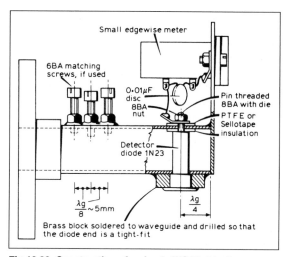

Fig 10.30. Construction of a simple WG16 detector

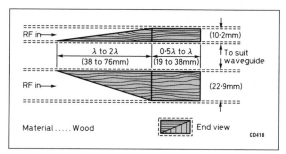

Fig 10.31. Construction of a WG16 load from a piece of tapered wood. The dimensions given are for 10GHz and WG16

waveguide and between the nut/solder-tag and the out-side surface of the guide wall.

The diode is matched into the waveguide by adjusting the three matching screws for maximum current output with RF input at the chosen operating frequency.

The approximate measurement of power, using diode detectors, was discussed earlier and graphs given which showed output power related to detector current. Used with care, your measurements will be accurate to within a milliwatt or so.

Matched loads

A matched waveguide load can be made from a short-circuited length of WG16, a flange, and a shaped piece of wood as shown in Fig 10.31. Solder on the flange and the short-circuit plate first. The wood is tapered as shown and should be a good fit into the waveguide. It can be glued in place in the shorted waveguide or, if it is a really tight fit, simply pushed down into place. A load like this can be used to absorb power, either in test equipment or at the open end of a piece of waveguide.

Some surplus professional WG16 loads are shown in Fig 10.32 and other 10GHz (coaxial) loads are shown in Fig 10.33. The advantage of coaxial loads is that they can be used at any frequency *below* their maximum frequency, whereas waveguide loads cannot, since waveguide always has a lower 'cut-off frequency' below which it will not work.

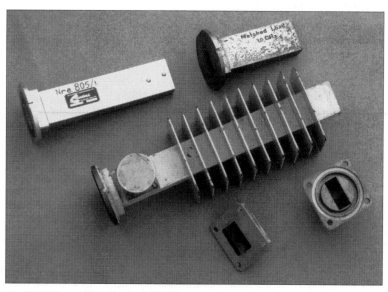

Fig 10.32. Some WG16 loads *(G3PFR)*

Fig 10.33. Some surplus 10GHz coaxial loads *(G3PFR)*

Waveguide variable attenuators

These are very useful in test equipment where they can be used to absorb part of the power output from an oscillator so that a detector is not overdriven (too much current) or to provide isolation between the oscillator and a wavemeter to prevent pulling while measuring frequency. Such a set-up was described earlier – see Fig 10.16. A typical variable waveguide attenuator is shown in Fig 10.34.

Wavemeters for 10GHz

High-*Q* absorption wavemeters of several makes can sometimes be found as surplus. It is possible to make wavemeters for this frequency range, although it is not easy for a beginner. Two designs are given in detail in the RSGB *Microwave Handbook*: both need the use of a lathe and so will not be described here. It is probably less expensive to buy a surplus wavemeter than to try to build one, since the micrometer screw needed to make a wavemeter is expensive. Two wavemeters, one home-made and one surplus professional, are shown in Fig 10.35.

Until you have a wavemeter, you'll have to rely on the simple method of frequency measurement described earlier. You really need the help of someone with a proper

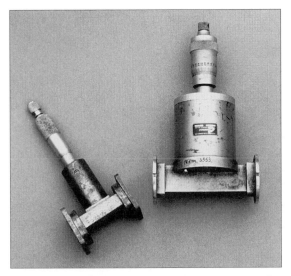

Fig 10.35. Two cavity absorption wavemeters. The smaller wavemeter is home-made and the larger one is a surplus professional type by Sanders Microwave *(G3PFR)*

wavemeter to check your results, although if you are operating well away from the band edges (as you should be), the simple method can give results accurate enough to satisfy the regulations.

Coaxial to waveguide transitions

Coaxial cables are not much used at 10GHz, other than in very short lengths inside equipment to connect various 'bits' together, because of the high losses involved compared with waveguide. Losses of various coaxial lines and their connectors were given in Tables 10.1 and 10.2. Andrew Heliax can be useful, for example Andrew FHJ4-50 shows a loss of about 4dB per 20ft and short lengths of ordinary flexible cable with N-type connectors may sometimes be found, particularly in older X-band equipment. It is more likely that short 0.141in (3.58mm) semi-rigid coaxial leads terminated in SMA connectors will be found on more modern equipment. It is useful to have one or two coaxial to waveguide transitions available when experimenting with PCB mounted circuits or some of the more recent professional equipment appearing on the surplus market. Two types are described.

A coaxial (N-type) to WG16 transition

N-type connectors are rated up to about 10GHz and can be used successfully, although there is a slight risk of over-moding in the connectors or the cable (eg a short length of FHJ4-50) used with them. The use of conventional cables is not advised because the losses involved are high and the flexible nature of the cable can lead to unpredictable impedance changes. However, some of the

Fig 10.34. Typical waveguide variable attenuator *(G3PFR)*

older surplus X-band equipments are fitted with these connectors.

A small (square) flange N-type socket should be chosen. The dimensions of the flange are 18 × 18mm with 13mm fixing centres for 3mm screws. The solder spill is usually 3mm in diameter and hollow. The insulation carrying the centre pin is normally held in place by a spun collar or rim of metal which sticks out below the flange and goes through a clearance hole in the panel on which the socket is mounted. This collar is normally deeper than the thickness of the waveguide wall (0.05in, 1.27mm) and would protrude into the waveguide if mounted with the flange flush on the waveguide surface. The diameter of the solder spill is also bigger than needed. Thus, the socket needs modification before it can be used easily. Occasionally, surplus sockets can be found which do not have this rim; they may also have an elongated, solid metal 'spill'. This type of socket is very easy to modify, as all that is required is that the spill is turned or filed down to the required diameter and then cut to length.

First the 'rim' around the insulation on the back of the socket is removed, by careful filing or sawing, to enable the socket to fit flush with the waveguide face. This may cause the dielectric bearing the pin to become loose in the socket, so care is needed. In the final assembly, the dielectric will be held in place by compression against the outer surface of the waveguide to which the socket is attached. The dielectric is cut back flush with the flange surface, using a sharp knife or scalpel (care!).

Next the spill is modified by cutting it almost flush with the dielectric and soldering a 1mm diameter probe of stiff copper wire of the required length in place of the original spill.

So that the socket can be mounted on the waveguide without complicating construction, the probe spacing from the WG short has been increased by $\lambda_g/2$, from 0.12 × λ_g to 0.62 × λ_g, ie to 23.1mm. This allows the use of a simple, soldered end plate as the WG short. The probe enters the waveguide through a hole a little smaller in diameter than the measured diameter of the dielectric, so that the insulation carrying the centre pin of the socket is firmly held in place between the socket body and the waveguide wall.

The modified socket can be fixed to the waveguide by soldering or, better, by means of 3mm screws inserted into tapped holes in the waveguide wall. If this method of fixing is used, then the fixing screws should be trimmed in length so that they end up flush with the inner face of the guide wall. This has the advantage that the socket is easily removable for trimming the length of the probe during testing.

The use of a larger-than-optimum diameter probe will increase the effective bandwidth of the transition. This does not matter much in amateur equipment, but you

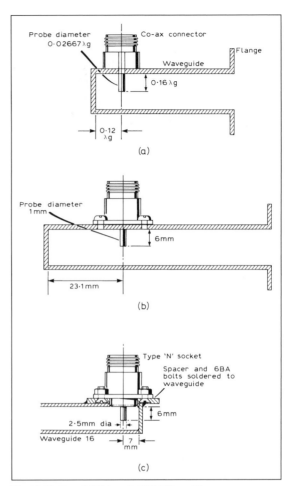

Fig 10.36. Coaxial N-type to WG16 transition

might need to experiment with the *length* of the probe for best match and signal transfer. The construction of an N-type transition is given in Fig 10.36 and a photograph of a surplus professional N-type to WG16 transition is given in Fig 10.37.

A coaxial (SMA) to WG16 transition

SMA connectors can be used up to 18GHz and are used with 0.141in (3.58mm) semi-rigid coaxial 'cables'. These connectors should be the first choice for this band. An ordinary SMA socket should be used for this design. This normally has a solder spill which is 1.3mm diameter and 6.5mm long.

There is no need to make the diameter of the spill smaller as this diameter will still provide a reasonable match. The dielectric does not protrude behind the mounting flange and needs no modification. The hole necessary to match the dielectric of the socket is 4mm diameter.

Fig 10.37. Left: probe-coupled home-made SMA to WG16 transition, dimensions as shown in Fig 10.38. Centre: end-coupled SMA to WG16 transition. Right: surplus N-type to WG16 transition. *(G3PFR)*

Fig 10.38(b). WG16 to SMA transition (G3PFR). Photo: G6WWM

It is possible to mount the socket on the waveguide with 4.25mm spacing from the end short, provided that it is soldered in place. If four fixing screws are used, then this distance must be increased to about 5.5mm to be able to fit the rear two screws. Although this is slightly greater than the optimum, it has been found to make little difference in practice. If screws are used they should be M1.5, cut so that they do not protrude into the waveguide. Dimensions for 10,380MHz are given in Fig 10.38. None is very critical: slight mismatching can be corrected by adjusting the three-screw tuner. A good match with wider bandwidth was still obtained with the probe diameter increased to 3mm by means of a soldered sleeve.

Waveguide switches

Switching is not needed if you use an in-line Gunn oscillator/mixer as your transmitter and receiver. If you use separate transmitters and receivers, you will need some kind of switching to get you from transmit to receive.

Rotary waveguide change-over switches can sometimes be found as surplus and may look like Fig 10.39. They are rather too difficult for most amateurs to make and so are best bought if needed.

Coaxial switches

Like rotary waveguide switches, these also are almost impossible for amateurs to make. Recently, quite large numbers of coaxial (SMA) switches, for use up to 18GHz, have become available on the surplus market. Keep your eyes open at rallies and other amateur exhibitions if you need a suitable relay for transmit/receive switching, especially with narrow-band transmitters and receivers! Fig 10.40 is a typical 18GHz surplus professional coaxial SMA switch.

Simple 'plug and socket' switching

Manual switching can be used, although it may be slow, by using round flanges and locking rings of the type described earlier. Change over can be made rather easier if the 'male' locating ring is fixed in position on its flange by the use of superglue, for it is often difficult in the field, with cold fingers, to handle both the rings and the equipment simultaneously!

Directional couplers

These are used to 'sample' power from the main waveguide (or rigid coaxial line) or to divide the power between two waveguides (or rigid coaxial lines). The coupling between the main guide/line and the coupled guide/line can be

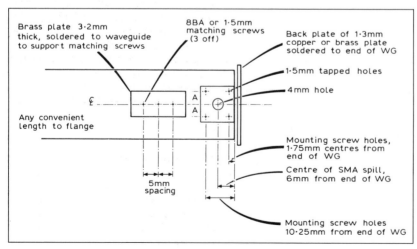

Fig 10.38(a). Diagram of WG16 to SMA transition

Brass plate 3·2mm thick, soldered to waveguide to support matching screws

8BA or 1·5mm matching screws (3 off)

Back plate of 1·3mm copper or brass plate soldered to end of WG

1·5mm tapped holes

4mm hole

Any convenient length to flange

Mounting screw holes, 1·75mm centres from end of WG

Centre of SMA spill, 6mm from end of WG

5mm spacing

Mounting screw holes 10·25mm from end of WG

Fig 10.39. Waveguide rotary change-over switch

almost any value, expressed in decibels. 3dB, 6dB and 10dB couplers, both coaxial and waveguide, are quite common in test equipment: a 3dB coupler transfers exactly half the power from the main waveguide into the coupled guide, a 6dB coupler transfers one quarter and a 10dB coupler one tenth. Lower coupling (maybe 10 to 30dB) is often used in receivers to transfer some of the

Fig 10.40. Typical surplus SMA-coaxial changeover relay, made by Sivers Lab (Philips, Sweden), rated to 18GHz *(G3PFR)*

Fig 10.41. Surplus wide-band Microline™ coaxial directional coupler by Narda Microwave Corp, USA. This 10dB coupler is rated within ±0.4dB over the range 1 to 12.4GHz. Input socket left; output socket right; −10dB coupled output top left; coupled line low-power terminating load top right. The coupler can be used between a transmitter and the antenna as an 'in-line' power indicator, or the output can be terminated in a 50Ω RF load as part of a test rig. A very useful piece of test gear for both the 1.3 and 10GHz bands! *(G3PFR)*

Fig 10.42. Two waveguide couplers. The 3dB coupler on the left is a surplus type. The 13dB cross-coupler on the right is home-made *(G3PFR)*

transmitter power to give a local oscillator input to a receiver mixer.

While waveguide couplers can be made at home, they are not easy to make accurately and again, it is easier for the beginner to buy ready-made, surplus couplers if these are needed. A surplus professional wide-band (1GHz to 12.4GHz) coaxial coupler is shown in Fig 10.41. Two typical waveguide couplers are shown in Fig 10.42. The larger 3dB WG16 coupler is surplus professional and the other, a 13dB cross-coupler, is home-made.

Appendix 1

Tools and how to use them

Choosing tools

If you do not have many tools, you will need to beg or buy some. Unfortunately they can be rather expensive, and this section is intended to help you get as much as possible for your money. It is not always best to look for the lowest price as many cheap tools do not perform well, even when new. The tools are described in the order which, in the opinion of the author, indicates their importance to a beginner in home construction but other people may well have other ideas of the priority.

Soldering iron

There are many small types available at a price of about £7 to £8. Look for the power; it should be in the range 15 to 25W. The higher power would probably be best for those who have not soldered before. Choose one which has interchangeable bits and a range of these available for the iron you select. The bits have points with a width ranging from about 1mm up to 6mm. You will not need all of them at first and one 1 to 2mm and a second 5mm would be fine. When you buy the iron, check that a suitable stand is also on offer. There are some kits that include an iron, a stand, some solder and a booklet giving very useful hints on soldering. The iron in the photograph is one of the Antex range.

Wire cutters

These most important tools are used almost continuously during construction work. Again there are many types on offer at prices ranging from £1 to £20! Sometimes the very cheap ones are adequate, but always test them or ask for them to be tested by cutting the wire ends of a resistor and a transistor (the lead-out wires of transistors are usually steel). They must cut right through the wire with a snap,

Fig A1.2. Wire cutters

Fig A1.3. A lower-priced type of wire cutter

not squeeze it very thin or even worse, twist the wire sideways. Sometimes cutters will work on iron wire and not on copper, and this is why two components were suggested for the test.

The better cutters and some types of pliers often have a joint similar to that shown in the photograph (Fig A1.2).

These are called 'box joints'; they cost about £10 to £20 but are excellent and will last forever if treated carefully – do not try to cut very thick copper wire or iron more than about 1mm. Do look out for this type in the secondhand shops etc – you might be lucky and find a secondhand pair of cutters made by Lindstrom.

A good but much cheaper cutter looks like the one shown in Fig A1.3. This has what is known as a 'lap joint'. Many of this type have a safety clip which holds the end of the cut wire and stops it flying. The cutter shown in the photograph is one made by Cooper Tools and costs about £4.50. Again there are many types and

Fig A1.1. A simple soldering iron and stand

Fig A1.4. A terminal screwdriver

Fig A1.5. A Phillips screwdriver

sizes but the larger side cutters used by electricians are not really suitable.

Screwdrivers

Most households have a screwdriver of some sort. You will need a thin one with about 2 to 3mm across the end of the blade, something like the one in the picture. This is called a 'terminal screwdriver' and costs about 20 pence. It can be used for many jobs including tightening the grub screws in control knobs and in terminal blocks. A medium-size driver will also be useful, with about 5mm across the blade.

One other screwdriver is worth looking for at this stage – the cross-point, sometimes called 'Phillips' (Fig A1.5). The fixing screws of small plastic boxes are of this type. Choose a small one so that it will fit the small screws used.

Hand drill

Holes will need to be made quite early on during construction projects. For the beginner, a hand drill similar to the one in the photograph is probably best. The drill bit (twist drill) is more likely to do what is wanted than it would if a power drill was used. In any case, cost is important and even a small hand drill can cost £10. It might be worthwhile paying another visit to the market stall or secondhand tool shop – perhaps a car boot sale!

First make sure that the gears run smoothly with no

Fig A1.6. A hand drill and bit

grinding or slipping. Then check the chuck. This is the part which holds the bits. There are three little pieces of metal that open up and close as the outside is turned. Make sure they do! Try to hold a thin nail about twice as thick as a dressmaking pin. If the nail falls out, don't buy it. Finally open the jaws (the three pieces of metal inside the chuck) by turning the outside of the chuck. If the pieces flop about or fall back into the chuck, don't buy it. The general rule is: the lower the asking price, the closer you must examine it.

Fig A1.7. Taper reamers

Now hopefully you have managed to get a drill so you will need some twist drills (bits). Again these can be rather expensive. Unless you know something about drills it would be advisable to buy new ones, so give the secondhand shop a miss for these. However, there is a way to avoid too much outlay – start with just three bits, one each of 6mm or 1/4in (probably the biggest that the drill will accept), 3mm or 1/8in and 1.5mm or 1/16in. They should cost between £1 and £2 for the three.

Taper reamer

One of these is worth a box of drill bits. There are two sizes generally available and the picture shows what they look like. They allow a small hole in sheet metal or plastic to be made larger. At the same time it ensures that the final hole will be round! It often surprises the inexperienced constructor to find that larger drills tend to make holes in thin sheets which are almost triangular.

The smaller reamer will enter a hole of 3mm or more and by gentle turning will enlarge it up to 12mm if necessary. If kept for use on aluminium and plastic, it will last for a long time but less if used on steel. It costs about £4, which may seem a lot. However, if you try to buy one 12mm twist drill you will probably have to pay £2 and in any case your hand drill would not accept one. The larger reamer needs a hole of 6mm and will enlarge up to 25mm. Start with the smaller one. Reamers are obtainable from Cirkit or Bonex (see Appendix 2).

Hacksaw (Fig A1.8)

If a full-size hacksaw frame is available, all you need is one or two fine blades; 24 teeth per inch should be satisfactory for most jobs. Be sure to put the blade in the frame so that the arrow on the blade points is in the

Fig A1.8. A junior hacksaw

direction in which the saw is pushed. In other words, the saw must cut as you push it away from you.

If you are not so lucky and have to buy there are a number of advantages in the junior hacksaw.

The saw and replacement blades are much cheaper and it is easier to handle than its 'big brother' because it is smaller and lighter. Some very cheap ones are available and are quite useful, but if possible get one with a blade tension screw as in the illustration. Usually with this type of junior hacksaw it is possible to turn the blade through 90° so that long strips of metal or copper laminate can be cut.

Also this type will enable a sawing wire to be used in the place of a blade. It is a long, thin round file and enables the saw to move in any direction so that rectangular (or any other shape) holes can be cut in sheet material. The sawing wire cannot be fitted to a frame which does not have a tension screw, so it may worthwhile paying a little more so that the extra facility will be available if required in the future. Sawing wires or 'Abrafile' are obtainable for full-size frames but they are much dearer and they break easily!

Modelling knife

A small one is very useful in preparing the ends of insulated wires, cutting Veroboard and copper laminate and in fact a whole host of jobs – you probably have one already.

Needle files

These are very small files and can be bought in sets or singly. The most useful is a round one, which is about 3mm across the thickest part, tapering down to a sharp point. It can be used to correct the position of a hole that has been drilled just a little to one side of the correct place. It is surprising how often that happens! Or it can be used to make a hole in a PCB or Veroboard just a little larger. Take care when using needle files – the name is very 'pointed'! Also the point breaks very easily.

There are many other tools you may need but aim to build up your kit gradually.

Cutting copper laminate

This can be done using a hacksaw if the width or length of the required piece is not too great. Turning the hacksaw blade through 90° will help if thin strips are needed but care is needed to stop the material sliding about as it is cut. A broken blade is often the result unless the board

is held securely. The edges will not be perfectly straight after sawing and will need to be cleaned up by means of a fine file. Altogether the operation is rather time consuming and often frustrating.

An alternative method (normally used by the author) is similar to glass cutting. Use a sharp modelling knife and a steel rule to score the material so that the copper coating is cut completely through to the laminate. Mark the position of the cut on the reverse side and score on the plain side or the other copper side if double-sided board is being used. As with glass cutting, the next step requires courage. Hold the board in the jaws of a vice or a work bench such as a Workmate so that the score marks are in line with the edge of the vice. Apply pressure to the surface over as much area as possible, bending the board against the edge of the clamp. If all is well it will break (with a tearing sound) along the lines scribed.

The process works better when glassfibre board is being cut but is generally successful with all types of substrates (the material which supports the copper). The edges still need a little cleaning up but at least they are straight. Practice using some scrap board before proceeding to cut a working piece. If you are preparing a printed circuit board, cut the board to size before etching and drilling.

The tracks and the holes tend to dictate the position of the break if it is attempted after the board is almost complete. This can be quite traumatic after a great deal of work.

It is most important that a sharp knife with a pointed blade is used and that the copper is cut completely.

Cutting aluminium sheet

This is much more difficult and is often the major reason for constructors opting for a ready-made box. However this need not be the case as there are a number of ways in which the problem can be overcome.

Some suppliers, such as Badger Boards, may be prepared to supply aluminium sheets cut to your specified size and gauge, but you must remember that the cost of this service, together with post and packing, may well be near to that of a commercial box.

If you live in or near a town (even a small one) it is worth looking through Yellow Pages for small engineering firms. Many of these, if involved with aluminium sheet, often have offcuts from which your pieces could be cut, and sometimes they will be prepared to cut your pieces in the guillotine. You must be careful to give the exact sizes. Remember the most important saying – "Measure twice, mark once and cut once". Ask the cost first and then decide if the exercise is economic.

18-gauge aluminium can be cut by means of tin snips but it is hard on the hands and the finished article is not very flat. For small pieces some success can be had if the following method is adopted. Mark the piece to be cut, then cut it out by using the tin snips about 3mm from the line, resulting in the piece being a little too big. Now carefully follow the line using the tin snips so that the part of the metal you want lies flat along the lower of the blades. In this way the curl from the first cut will be removed and the resulting piece will be almost flat. Like many operations a little practice is worth many hundreds of words.

Sawing the sheet is another possibility. The hacksaw can be used but the size is limited by the presence of the frame. Turning the blade through 90° sometimes helps but the width of the piece is now limited to the depth of the frame. If you are lucky enough to possess a jig saw then your main problem is following your lines. Then there will be considerable work with a file to get the edges smooth and straight.

Nuts and screws

A little knowledge of these will enable the correct choice to be made when using these. Fig A1.9 summarises some of the more important points. There are two basic systems in use in the UK.

The Imperial system uses a measurement known as 'BA' (British Association). The screws and nuts are normally obtainable in sizes from 0BA (about ¼in) to 8BA (about ¹⁄₁₆in). Normally only the even number sizes are used but all are available.

The other system is Isometric where the outside diameter of the screw is quoted in millimetres with an 'M' proceeding the number. For example, M2.5 is a screw (or nut) with an outside diameter of 2.5mm. The gauge in Fig A1.9(a) compares the diameters of the screws in the two systems. Some of the screws and nuts seem to be almost identical in the two systems but they are not – mixing Imperial screws with metric nuts will result in a jam or stripped threads.

It is important that the screws used be of the correct length. When assembled the screw should just extend beyond the edge of the nut as shown in Fig A1.9(c). In some applications a screw which is too long will cause fault conditions. An example is the fixing screws used with a miniature tuning capacitor of the type used in the projects described in Chapters 2, 3 and 8. If these are fixed by means of screws which are too long, the plates of the capacitor will be shorted and probably mechanically damaged.

It is easy to cut a screw – a large pair of wire cutters will do the job but it will be impossible to get the nut to screw on afterwards. The best technique is illustrated in Fig A1.9(d). A nut is threaded on to the screw and the piece to be cut off is held in the jaws of a vice. Any

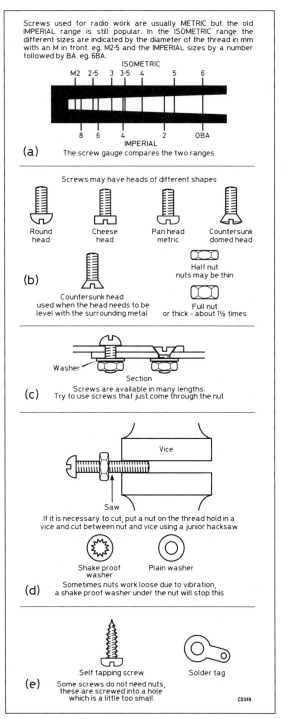

Fig A1.9. Nuts and screws and things. (a) Comparison of Imperial and Isometric sizes. (b) Various types of screw heads. (c) Using screws and bolts. (d) How to cut screws, plus an introduction to washers. (e) Self-tapping screws

damage to the thread will not matter as the part held is to be cut off. Use a fine blade in the hacksaw (a junior hacksaw is most suitable) to cut the screw between the nut and the vice. Hold both nut and screw in the vice to allow the cut end to be smoothed, using a fine file which is used at about 45° and moved away from the head of the screw. Remove from the vice and separate nut and screw – any roughness on the cut end will be removed by the nut as it comes off the end of the screw.

Note the various types of screw head available shown in Fig A1.9(b) – the round head and countersunk head are probably most commonly used.

Self-tapping screws (Fig A1.9(e)) are very useful when it is difficult or impossible to get to the other side of the work to put on a nut. When using these, try a few test holes in a scrap piece of material to be used. If the hole is too big the screw will tear the material and fail to hold, but if it is too small it will be difficult to drive the screw in. It is possible to find the drill size from tables but it is generally easier and quicker to do a test drilling.

Both nuts and screws are expensive to buy and constructors are advised to save any from equipment which is being stripped for components – the screws are often neglected and thrown away with the debris.

If a screw is to be passed through a hole which is in an almost inaccessible position, the following tip may help. Push a small piece of wax (eg from a candle) on to the head of the screw and then 'stick' it to the head of the screwdriver. The screw can now be carefully inserted through the hole.

Terminal pins

"First insert the terminal pins". Many constructional articles contain this statement but very few give any help in carrying out this fiddly and sometimes very difficult task.

Certainly it is important that the pins be inserted before any components are fitted to the PCB, but the technique described will allow a pin to be fitted at any stage in the construction if one has been overlooked earlier. Pins are available in two types, both having a nominal diameter of 1mm with a splined section of about 1.5mm just below the head. Single-ended pins are more commonly used and provide a pin on the component side of the PCB. Double-ended pins have a 4mm section on both sides of the head. Both pins must be inserted so that the head is on the copper side of the board.

The plain section of the pin will pass easily into the hole – it is the splined section which requires considerable pressure to seat the head against the copper pad. A short piece of copper or steel tube of about 6mm outside diameter which is held in the jaws of a vice makes a very good support for the PCB while the pin is pressed in. Fig A1.10(a) should make the operation clear.

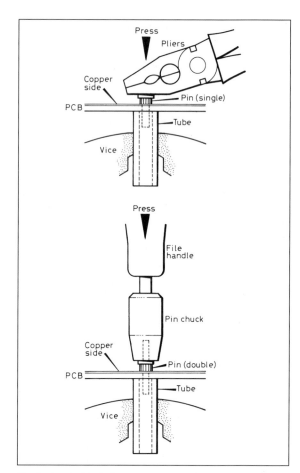

Fig A1.10. A simple jig makes pin insertion much easier

A double-sided pin is a little more difficult and some form of holder makes the job much easier. A pin pusher can be any piece of metal rod with a 1mm holed drilled in the end and fitted with a suitable handle. It sounds easy but, unless there is access to a lathe, it is almost impossible. A convenient pusher can be made from a small pin chuck which is pushed into a small file handle. Again reference to Fig A1.10(b) should make everything clear.

Making boxes

Ready-made boxes are expensive and a little hard work can save pounds. An aluminium box will almost always be satisfactory. Large projects and power supplies may require steel. Do not attempt to bend steel which is thicker than 19-gauge or, for aluminium, 18-gauge. A pair of bending bars will make the process easier and will last forever. Two pieces of angle iron 1.25 to 1.5in (30 to 40mm) and 12in long are required. Try to obtain pieces with smooth outside faces and rather sharp 90° corners. The bars need to have 0.25in (6mm) holes drilled at intervals so that 0.25in or 0BA bolts can be passed through to hold them together. It is most important that the holes in the two pieces should match and it would be advisable to get the help of an engineer to get these holes drilled. The spacing of the holes shown in Fig A1.11 will provide a range of six bolt intervals, allowing material of any width from a few millimetres to 250mm to be held with the bolts fairly close to the edges of the metal.

Clamp the metal to be bent between the bars with the fixing bolts as close as possible. The bending line should be in line with the edge of the bars. Hold the assembly in a vice or Workmate-type bench. Use a block of wood or large file to bend the metal towards the bending line. Fig A1.11 shows the method of use.

The secret of a good bend is to keep the file or block of wood as close as possible to the point where the metal emerges from the bending bars. Much more force will be needed but avoid moving further away from the bars; it will be much easier but a rounded bend will result. A block of hard wood held against the bend will allow the bend to be completed by means of a few hammer blows while the wood prevents any damage to the aluminium.

The box required for both the 3.5MHz CW transmitter and the Top Band DSB transmitter is described in Chapters 5 and 7, and the one for the FM transmitter in Chapter 8.

Bending the long edges of both the base and the cover should present no difficulty but the 12mm flange on the short sides of the base is quite difficult. A simple solution is arrived at by the use of two pieces of 12mm (^{1}/$_2$in) aluminium angle bolted to the base to act as the flange. The cutting detail will need to be modified by leaving

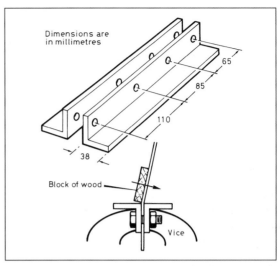

Fig A1.11. Bending bars which will last a lifetime

off the two 124mm by 12mm sections at each side of the base.

The angle will need to be drilled (3mm holes) at each end and the holes marked through onto the base. The edge of the angle must be flush with the edge of the base. Bolt them to the base using 6BA or M2.5 screws and nuts. The heads of the screws must be on the underside of the base. There is no need to use countersunk head screws as the rubber feet will give enough clearance for the heads. The position of the holes in the side of the angle for the cover fixing screws should be marked after the cover has been made and drilled.

The cost of the home-made box is only a fraction of that of the ready-made one.

Appendix 2

Suppliers of components

Almost all of the suppliers listed will provide a catalogue, many of them free of charge. You should try to get as many as possible as they often give valuable data about components in addition to giving their availability and cost.

At the time of writing this book, UHF and microwave components were not easy to get from the usual amateur suppliers. It was also often difficult to get suitable components in small quantities from some of the larger suppliers. Some components are available from 'surplus' sources and these are given *where they are known to be reliable*.

Other components, such as surplus waveguide components, can often be obtained from rallies, although there will usually be no guarantee that such components will work properly. The chances are that waveguide 'hardware', unless obviously damaged, *will* work properly. Things like attenuators and wavemeters may need recalibrating although, in the authors' experience, even this is unlikely unless you want to carry out very precise measurements.

The list of suppliers that follows was current at the time of going to press (1995). The list is not complete and there are many more suppliers. Those in the list are known to supply in small quantities or to supply PCBs for the various projects described. Other suppliers, not included in this list, may be prepared to supply on these terms – *ask them!*

Badger Boards,
87 Blackberry Lane,
Four Oaks,
Sutton Coldfield B74 4JF.
Tel: 0121-353 9326.
(PCBs for various designs.)

J Birkett,
25 The Strait,
Lincoln,
Lincs LN2 1JF.
Tel: 01522 520767.
(Surplus GaAsFETs, Gunn diodes and oscillators, microwave mixer diodes.)

Bonex,
12 Elder Way,
Langley Business Park,
Slough,
Berks SL3 6EP.
Tel: 01753 549502.
(Toko inductors and trimmer capacitors, some chip components, Avantek MMICS and GaAsFETs, general miniature components.)

British Amateur Television Club,
Membership Secretary David Lawton (G0ANO),
'Grenehurst',
Pinewood Road,
High Wycombe,
Bucks HP12 4DD.
Tel: 01494 28899.
(Members' services include CQ-TV quarterly journal, other publications, book library and reprints, PCBs, camera spares, operating contests and awards, video library, technical advice.)

Cirkit Distribution Ltd,
Park Lane,
Broxbourne,
Herts EN10 7NQ.
Tel: 01992 441306.
(Catalogue from W H Smith. Wide range of general miniature components, some UHF transistors and Gunn modules, RF connectors.)

Electromail,
PO Box 33,
Corby,
Northants NN17 9EL.
Tel: 01536 204555.
(Very large catalogue, identical to RS Components. Wide range of general components. SMDs and silver-loaded solder.)

Electrovalue Ltd,
28 St Judes Road,
Englefield Green,
Egham, Surrey TW20 0YB.
Tel: 01784 433603.
(Components and ferrites.)

European Microwave Components Ltd,
7 Freebournes Court,
Newland Street,
Witham, Essex CM8 2BL.
Tel: 01376 515200.
(Wide range of microwave components: solid-state devices, connectors and adaptors, coaxial/waveguide transitions.)

Farnell Electronic Components,
Canal Road,
Leeds LS12 2TU.
Tel: 0113 2636311.
(Very large catalogue. Wide range of general components, range of microwave connectors/semi-rigid coaxial cable.)

Golledge Electronics Ltd,
Merriott,
Somerset TA16 5NS.
Tel: 01460 73718.
(Crystals.)

C M Howes Communications,
Eydon, Daventry,
Northamptonshire NN11 6PT.
Tel: 01327 60178.
(Receiver and transmitter kits for beginners.)

Jandek,
6 Fellows Avenue,
Kingswinford,
West Midlands DY6 9ET.
Tel: 01384 288900.
(Kits and components.)

Kanga Products,
Sea View House,
Crete Road East,
Folkestone,
Kent CT18 7EG.
Tel: 01303 891106.
(Kits and components.)

LMW Electronics Ltd,
12, Bidford Road,
Braunstone,
Leicester LE3 3AE.
Tel: 0116 2630038.
(Microwave converter and transverter kits, semiconductors and other UHF/microwave components.)

Mainline Electronics,
P O Box 235,
Leicester LE2 9SH.
Tel: 0116 2777648.
(Semiconductors, components. 'No-tune' transverter PCBs.)

Maplin Electronics,
PO Box 3,
Rayleigh,
Essex SS9 8LR.
Tel: 01702 552911.
(Catalogue from W H Smith. Wide range of general miniature components.)

McKnight Crystals Ltd,
Hadley Industrial Estate,
Hythe,
Southampton SO4 6ZY.
Tel: 01703 848961.
(Crystals made to order.)

Piper Communications,
4 Severn Road,
Chilton,
Didcot,
Oxon OX11 0PW.
Tel: 01234 834328.
(Range of UHF and microwave semiconductors, range of UHF and microwave components, tinplate project boxes for many of the designs described here.)

Quartslab Marketing Ltd,
P O Box 19,
Erith,
Kent DA8 1LH.
Tel: 01322 330830.
(Crystals made to order.)

P G Sergent, G4ONF,
6 Gurney Close,
Costessey,
Norwich,
Norfolk NR5 0NB
Tel: 01603 747782.
(Wide-range wavemeter (144MHz to 2500MHz), cavity block for self-calibrating 10GHz wavemeter.)

RSGB Microwave Committee Components Service,
314A Newton Road,
Rushden,
Northants NN10 0SY.
Tel: 01933 411446.
(PCBs and special components for designs described here, in other RSGB books or by the designers, G3WDG and G4DDK. Discount prices for RSGB members.)

Index

Some other RSGB publications . . .

❏ **AMATEUR RADIO OPERATING MANUAL**

Covers the essential operating techniques required for most aspects of amateur radio including DX, contests and mobile operation, and features a comprehensive set of operating aids.

❏ **MICROWAVE HANDBOOK**

A major publication in three volumes. Volume I covers operating techniques, system analysis and propagation, antennas, transmission lines and components, semiconductors and valves. Volume 2 continues with construction techniques, common equipment, beacons and repeaters, test equipment, safety, filters and data. Volume 3 concludes with practical equipment designs for each band.

❏ **PRACTICAL ANTENNAS FOR NOVICES**

This guide is written especially for newly qualified holders of the Novice Licence, and describes in detail how to build simple but effective antennas for each of the Novice bands up to 434MHz.

❏ **THE RADIO AMATEUR'S GUIDE TO EMC**

Helps you avoid electromagnetic compatibility (EMC) problems by practising good radio housekeeping, and assists you in the diagnosis and cure of any which do occur. The social dimension is not forgotten, and a whole chapter is devoted to dealing with neighbours. If trouble ever does come to your door, you can reach confidently for this book.

❏ **RADIO COMMUNICATION HANDBOOK**

First published in 1938 and a favourite ever since, this large and comprehensive guide to the theory and practice of amateur radio takes the reader from first principles right through to such specialised fields as packet radio, slow-scan television and amateur satellite communication.

❏ **TEST EQUIPMENT FOR THE RADIO AMATEUR**

Explains the principles of measurement techniques, and gives constructional details of many items of up-to-date equipment of interest not only to the radio amateur but also to the electronics enthusiast.

❏ **VHF/UHF MANUAL**

The standard UK textbook on the theory and practice of amateur radio transmission and reception at VHF and UHF includes full constructional details of many items of equipment.

 RADIO SOCIETY OF GREAT BRITAIN
Lambda House, Cranborne Road,
Potters Bar, Herts EN6 3JE, England

Get more out of amateur radio ...
... as an RSGB member!

Radio Communication

A magazine which covers a wide range of interests and which features the best and latest amateur radio news. The Society's journal has acquired a worldwide reputation for its content. With 100 pages, many in colour, 'RadCom' strives to maintain its reputation as the best available and is circulated free of charge to members throughout the world.

The regular columns in the magazine include those for HF, VHF/UHF, microwave, SWL, clubs, satellite, data and contests. In addition to the many technical articles, the highly regarded 'Technical Topics' feature caters for those wishing to keep themselves briefed on recent developments in technical matters.

The 'Last Word' is a lively feature in which members can put forward their views and opinions and be sure of receiving a wide audience. To keep members in touch with what's going on in the hobby, events diaries are published each month.

Advertisements for the equipment you wish to sell can be placed in the magazine, with the advantages of short deadlines and large circulation.

QSL Bureau

Members enjoy the use of the QSL Bureau free of charge for both outgoing and incoming cards. This can save you a good deal of postage.

Special Event Callsigns

Special event callsigns in the GB series are handled by RSGB. They give amateurs special facilities for display-ing amateur radio to the general public.

Specialised News Sheets

The RSGB publishes the weekly *DX News-sheet* for HF enthusiasts and the *Microwave Newsletter* for those operating above 1GHz.

Specialised Equipment Insurance

Insurance for your valuable equipment which has been arranged specially for members. The rates are very advantageous.

Audio Visual Library

Films, audio and video tapes are available through one of the Society's Honorary Officers for all affiliated groups and clubs.

Reciprocal Licensing Information

Details are available for most countries on the RSGB computer database.

Government Liaison

One of the most vital features of the work of the RSGB is the ongoing liaison with the UK Licensing Authority – presently the Radiocommunications Agency (RA) of the Department of Trade and Industry. Setting and maintaining the proper framework in which amateur radio can thrive and develop is essential to the well-being of amateur radio. For example, the Novice Licence was introduced by the RA after long discussions with the RSGB. The Society also spares no effort in defence of amateur radio's most precious assets – the amateur bands.

Beacons and Repeaters

The RSGB supports financially all repeaters and beacons which are looked after by the appropriate committee of the Society, ie 1.8–30MHz by the HF Committee, 30–1000MHz (1GHz) by the VHF Committee and frequencies above 1GHz by the Microwave Committee. For repeaters, the Society's Repeater Management Group has played a major role. Society books such as the *RSGB Amateur Radio Call Book* give further details, and computer-based lists giving operational status can be obtained by post from HQ.

Operating Awards

A wide range of operating awards are available via the responsible officers: their names can be found in the front pages of *Radio Communication* and in the *RSGB Amateur Radio Call Book*. Details of these awards can be found in the latter and also the *Amateur Radio Operating Manual* published by the Society.

Contests (HF/VHF/Microwave)

The Society has two contest committees which carry out all work associated with the running of contests. The HF Contests Committee deals with contests below 30MHz, whilst events on frequencies above 30MHz are dealt with by the VHF Contests Committee.

Morse Testing

The Society has responsibility for morse testing of radio amateurs in the UK. If you wish to take a morse test, write direct to RSGB HQ (Morse tests) for an application form.

Slow Morse

Many volunteers all over the country give up their time to send slow morse over the air to those who are preparing for the 5 and 12 words per minute morse tests. The Society also produces morse practice tapes.

RSGB Books

The Society publishes a range of books for the radio amateur and imports many others. Members are entitled to a discount on all books purchased from the Society. This discount can offset the cost of membership.

Propagation

The Society's Propagation Studies Committee is highly respected – both within the amateur community and professionally – for its work. Predictions are given in the weekly GB2RS news bulletins and the Society's monthly magazine *Radio Communication*.

Technical and EMC Advice

Although the role of the Society's Technical and Publications Advisory Committee is largely to vet material intended for publication, its members and HQ staff are always willing to help with any technical matters.

Breakthrough in domestic entertainment equipment can be a difficult problem to solve as well as having licensing implications. The Society's EMC Committee is able to offer practical assistance in many cases. The Society also publishes a special book to assist you. Additional advice can be obtained from the EMC Committee Chairman via RSGB HQ.

Planning Permission

There is a special booklet and expert help available to members seeking assistance with planning matters.

GB2RS

A special radio news bulletin transmitted each week and aimed especially at the UK radio amateur and short wave listener. The script is prepared each week by the Society's HQ staff. The transmission schedule appears in the *RSGB Amateur Radio Call Book*. The GB2RS bulletin is also sent out over the packet radio network.

RSGB Exhibitions and Mobile Rallies

The Society's Exhibition and Rally Committee organizes an annual exhibition and an annual mobile rally. Full details and a rally calendar can be found in *Radio Communication*.

RSGB Conventions

The Society's diary in *Radio Communication* contains details of all special conventions which are open to all radio amateurs. The Society holds several major conventions each year.

Observation Service

A number of leading national radio societies have volunteers who monitor the amateur bands as a service to the amateur community. Their task is to spot licence infringements and defective transmissions, and report them in a friendly way to the originating station.

Intruder Watch

This helps to protect the exclusive amateur bands by monitoring for stations not authorised to use them.

Send for our Membership Information Pack today and discover how you too can benefit from these services. Write to:

RADIO SOCIETY OF GREAT BRITAIN,
Lambda House, Cranborne Road,
Potters Bar, Herts EN6 3JE

Notes